> ☞ ‖ **Keep in mind...**
> ‖ **Begin where you are, but don't stay where you are.**

Adding Real Numbers

$$-7 + 3 = -4$$

1. 9 + (-6)

2. -54 + -6 + -3 + 42

3. -35 + 1 + -3 + 6

4. 4 + -15 + -13 + 19

5. 32 + -15 + 17

6. - 5 + 17 + (-6) + 4

7. 7 + 0 + -7

8. 11 + -5 + 17 + -5 + 3

9. 1.4 + (-7.2)

10. -1.6 + (-2.5)

11. 2.9 + -3.8

12. 6.25 + -3.45 + .50

13. $-9\frac{1}{3} + 4\frac{3}{4}$

14. $-3\frac{2}{3} + (-2\frac{1}{6}) + 3$

15. $-2\frac{1}{3} + 5\frac{3}{4}$

16. $7\frac{1}{3} + (-2\frac{5}{6})$

17. Susie had $500 in her savings account on Tuesday. She withdrew $200 on Wednesday, then deposited $350 on Thursday. What is the new balance in the account?

18. The temperature at 8:00 a.m. was -10° F. It rose 15° by noon. What was the temperature at noon?

Subtracting Real Numbers

$$7 - (-3) = 7 + 3 = 10$$

1. $32 - 212$

2. $19 - (-12)$

3. $-201 - (-42)$

4. $22 - 33 - (-11)$

5. $7 - (-5) - 6 - 7$

6. $33 - 14 - 42 + 16 - 26$

7. $0 - 14$

8. $7 - (-16)$

9. $-17 - 8$

10. $-9 - (-6)$

11. $2.9 - 3.8$

12. $8 - 3.2$

13. $12.3 - 6.7 - 3.5 + 1.8$

14. $-\dfrac{2}{3} - \dfrac{1}{12} - (-\dfrac{1}{4})$

15. $-\dfrac{3}{4} - \dfrac{1}{2}$

16. $-\dfrac{2}{3} - (-\dfrac{5}{6})$

17. The temperature is currently 9° F. At 9:00 a.m. this morning it was -3° F. What was the change in temperature?

18. The lowest temperature ever recorded in city A was -37° F. The lowest temperature ever recorded in city B was -63° F. Find the difference between the two temperatures.

Operations with Real Numbers

Multiplying Real Numbers

$$\left(-\frac{1}{2}\right)\left(-\frac{3}{4}\right)=\frac{3}{8}$$

1. $-4 \cdot 15$

2. $(-6)(-8)$

3. $(-10)(-3)(4)$

4. $(-21)(-4)(0)$

5. $(-3)(-3)(-3)$

6. $(-3)(8)$

7. $(-5)(0)$

8. $14(-6)$

9. -40×-9

10. $(6)(-8)(2)$

11. $(4)(-2)(-5)$

12. $(-7)(1.5)$

13. $(1.2)(-5)$

14. $(6.5)(1)(-3)$

15. $(-6)(-2.7)$

16. $\left(\frac{2}{3}\right)(-6)$

17. $(-2.3)(5)(-2)$

18. $\left(\frac{3}{8}\right)\left(\frac{5}{6}\right)$

19. $\left(-\frac{5}{8}\right)\left(-\frac{2}{3}\right)$

20. $\frac{1}{7}\left(-\frac{7}{10}\right)$

21. $(-12)\left(-\frac{1}{3}\right)\left(\frac{3}{4}\right)$

22. $\left(-6\frac{2}{3}\right)\left(3\frac{3}{4}\right)$

23. $(-4)^2$

24. $(-1)^3$

Dividing Real Numbers

$$-5.4 \div -9 = .6$$

1. $-91 \div 7$

2. $36 \div (-9)$

3. $-54 \div (-9)$

4. $75 \div 15$

5. $0 \div (-7)$

6. $\dfrac{56}{-7}$

7. $\dfrac{-72}{-12}$

8. $\dfrac{102}{-17}$

9. $600 \div 24$

10. $\dfrac{144}{-12}$

11. $-48 \div 3$

12. $-1.5 \div (-.3)$

13. $2.4 \div (-1.2)$

14. $-1.44 \div (.3)$

15. $\dfrac{0}{-4.12}$

16. $\dfrac{1}{8} \div -\dfrac{6}{5}$

17. $-\dfrac{3}{7} \div -\dfrac{8}{21}$

18. $-10 \div \dfrac{1}{3}$

19. $-\dfrac{3}{4} \div (-12)$

20. $-15 \div \dfrac{3}{5}$

21. $\dfrac{4}{5} \div (-\dfrac{3}{10})$

22. $-\dfrac{3}{8} \div (-\dfrac{3}{4})$

23. $\dfrac{5}{6} \div \dfrac{4}{9}$

24. $-6\dfrac{2}{3} \div 3\dfrac{3}{4}$

Order of Operations

$2 + (2^2 + 6) \div \text{-}2 - 1 = 2 + (4 + 6) \div \text{-}2 - 1 = 2 + 10 \div \text{-}2 - 1 = 2 + \text{-}5 - 1 = \text{-}4$

1. $(12 - 8) + 3$

2. $2 \cdot 6 + 4 \cdot 5$

3. $25 \div 5 \cdot 4 - 15 \cdot 8$

4. $3 + 15 \div 3 - 4$

5. $15 \div (7 - 2) + 3$

6. $2(7 + 3) \div 4$

7. $7 - (8 \cdot 2) \cdot 0$

8. $2(4 + (6 \div 2))$

9. $20 \div (2 + (7 - 4))$

10. $6(\text{-}9 + 4) \div 3 - 1$

11. $6 - 4(6 + 2)$

12. $12 \div ((8 \div 2) \cdot (3 \div 3))$

13. $\dfrac{9^2 - 11}{(3 + 4) \cdot 10}$

14. $\dfrac{3^2 - 4 \cdot 3 + 4}{3^2 - 4}$

15. $\dfrac{3 \cdot 2 \div 6 + 2 \cdot 3 \div 6}{3^2 + 2^2 + 1^2}$

16. $\dfrac{2 \cdot 4 - 6(2 + 1)}{1^2 - 3 \cdot 2}$

17. $\dfrac{(4 - 6)^2}{\text{-}24 \div 12}$

18. $\dfrac{2 \cdot 6 - (4 + 2)}{(\text{-}2 - 4 - 6) \div (2 - 1)}$

19. $\dfrac{\text{-}3(4 - 9)}{35 \div \text{-}7}$

20. $3^5 \div 3^2 \div 3^2 \div 3$

Opposites and Absolute Values

$$- (5c + 9d) = -5c - 9d \qquad -|7 - 9| = - |-2| = -2$$

1. $|-12|$

2. $- |5\frac{1}{2}|$

3. $|-5| + |9|$

4. $7 + |-3|$

5. $|7| + |-7|$

6. $- (-3 + 4)$

7. $- (9 - 9)$

8. $|9| - |-12|$

9. $|-3| + |9| - 6$

10. $-3 |5| - |5|$

11. $|-25| - |-14|$

12. $-18 + (- (-13))$

13. $|1 - 3| + 5$

14. $\dfrac{-|-3 + 5|}{-9 + (- (-1))}$

15. $- (2n - (-7))$

16. $- (-2x + -3y)$

17. $- (6x - 4y)$

18. $10m - (-2n)$

19. $-2 (3m^2 - 2m - 1)$

20. $-3 (4x - 6y)$

Real Numbers: Preparing for College

1. 1 – 3 equals

     a. -4   b. -2   c. 4   d. 2

2. If x and y are positive integers and if $\frac{x}{y} = 1$ and $(x + y)^2 = z$, which of the following can equal z?

     a. 5   b. 9   c. 16   d. 25

3. (-1) (-2) (-3) (+4) =

     a. -10   b. 24   c. -24   d. -36

4. (-2) – (-5) =

     a. -7   b. -3   c. 3   d. 7

5. (-5) + (-2) =

     a. -7   b. -3   c. 3   d. 7

6. $(\frac{1}{2}) \div (-\frac{7}{8}) =$

     a. $-\frac{4}{7}$ b. $-\frac{7}{16}$ c. $-1\frac{3}{4}$ d. $-2\frac{2}{7}$

7. 7 – ((-8) + (-2)) =

     a. -3   b. -1   c. 13   d. 17

8. $\left| \frac{(-18) + (-2)}{(7) + (-2)} \right|$

     a. $2\frac{2}{9}$ b. 4   c. $3\frac{1}{5}$ d. -4

9. The integers -2, -7, 5 and -5 written from least to greatest are:

     a. -2, -5, -7, 5   b. -5, -7, -2, 5   c. -7, -5, -2, 5   d. -7, -2, -5, 5

10. Which of the following conditions will make x – y a negative number?

     a. y > x   b. x > y   c. y > 0   d. x = y

☞ **Keep in mind...**
Triumph = Umph! added to Try

Combining Like Terms

| 8x + 5y + -17x = -9x + 5y |

1. 9x + 4x

2. 17 x + x

3. m + (-4m)

4. -7x – 8x

5. 14a – 19a

6. -a + 9a

7. 6xy + 5xy

8. -9m – m

9. 15a + (-11a)

10. -14x + 13x

11. $5x^2y + 13x^2y$

12. 21xy + (-9xy)

13. 17x + 1

14. 3.5y – 7.2y

15. -4.7y –2.3y

16. 3a + 5c – 9a

17. 2x – 9x + 7

18. 7x – 8 – 11x

19. 3x – 3y – 9x + 7y

20. 17x + 4 – 3x

21. 3x – 7y – 12y

22. 11a – 13a + 15a

23. 17x + 5a – 3x – 4a

24. 6x + 9y + 2x – 8y + 5

25. $3xy + 4xy + 5x^2y + 6xy^2$

26. -25y – 17y + 6xy – 3xy

...More Combining Like Terms

$$3(a + 2) + (2a - 6b) = 3a + 6 + 2a - 6b = 5a - 6b + 6$$

1. $5t + 3r + 9t - 10r - 8$

2. $4a + (-2b) + (-2a) + b$

3. $12x - 3y + x + 2y$

4. $-30x - (-1x)$

5. $6(x - y) - 3(3x + y)$

6. $17x + 3y + 30x - 5y$

7. $4p - 6q + 6q - 10p + q$

8. $-r + 7 + 3r - 9 - 2r$

9. $8(x + y) + 3(x - y)$

10. $3(x + 7y) - 5(x + 7y) + 9(x + 7y)$

11. $2(-2a^2 - 4d) - (-3a^2 + 17d)$

12. $2(3(-x^2 + x) - 1) - 5x + 6x^2$

13. $3(a + 2b) + - (b + 2a)$

14. $-5(a - b) - (a - b) + 8(a - b)$

15. $-4(x + 5(-3xy + x)) - (10 + 15xy)$

16. $\frac{5}{8}c^2 - \frac{1}{4}d - \frac{3}{7}c^2 + \frac{3}{5}d$

17. $3 \cdot 5a - 7 \cdot 3b - 3 \cdot 2a + 2 \cdot 9b$

18. $2\frac{1}{2}xy - xy + 3\frac{1}{3}xy$

19. $6(x^2 + y^2) - 7(x^2 + y^2)$

20. $4x - y + 2\frac{1}{2}x + 3\frac{1}{4}y$

Solving Equations with Addition and Subtraction

$$16 + x = -14$$
$$16 + -16 + x = -14 + -16$$
$$x = -30$$

1. $x + 7 = -13$

2. $x + 7 = 4$

3. $-14 + y = -17$

4. $y - 11 = 14$

5. $y - 5 = -7$

6. $-20 + x = -80$

7. $6 + x = 29$

8. $a + 32 = -4$

9. $-2 = x - 2$

10. $-19 + y = 42$

11. $16 = z - 10$

12. $y + 73 = 0$

13. $-100 = b + (-72)$

14. $w - 5 = (8 - 13)$

15. $x + 2.5 = -4.7$

16. $a + 3.6 = -.2$

17. $x - 6\frac{1}{4} = 12\frac{1}{2}$

18. $2\frac{1}{5} + x = -3\frac{1}{2}$

19. $n + \frac{1}{2} = \frac{3}{4}$

20. $b - 1\frac{1}{3} = -3\frac{5}{6}$

Solving Equations with Multiplication and Division

$$2x = 12$$
$$\frac{2x}{2} = \frac{12}{2}$$
$$x = 6$$

$$-\frac{3}{4}y = 15$$
$$-\frac{4}{3} \cdot -\frac{3}{4}y = 15 \cdot -\frac{4}{3}$$
$$y = -20$$

1. $3x = -21$

2. $-7y = 28$

3. $-28 = -196x$

4. $-15a = -45$

5. $-x = 17$

6. $-21 = -2x$

7. $-12b = -288$

8. $12x = -60$

9. $\frac{a}{5} = -6$

10. $-\frac{2}{5}y = -14$

11. $\frac{3x}{4} = -24$

12. $-\frac{x}{3} = \frac{4}{9}$

13. $-\frac{3}{7} = \frac{a}{14}$

14. $3a = -\frac{1}{4}$

15. $\frac{a}{2.4} = .26$

16. $-\frac{1}{99}y = 0$

17. $-1.5x = 6$

18. $-12.5 = 4n$

19. $-3.7w = -11.1$

20. $\frac{y}{6} = -\frac{2}{3}$

Solving Basic Combined Equations

$$7(x + 2) = -35$$
$$7x + 14 = -35$$
$$7x + 14 - 14 = -35 - 14$$
$$\frac{7x}{7} = \frac{-49}{7}$$
$$x = -7$$

1. $5x - 3 = 22$

2. $4a + 3 = -5$

3. $5 - 7y = 33$

4. $5x - 11 = -16$

5. $-3 = 5x + 12$

6. $0 = .6x - 3.6$

7. $6 - 8x = -26$

8. $5 = 5x + 27$

9. $3(w + 3) = -15$

10. $2(y + 1) - 5 = 7$

11. $6 - \frac{2}{3}x = -8$

12. $.3x - 4.2 = 2.7$

13. $8.6 = 2.1 - 1.3y$

14. $5 - 4(y + 1) = -3$

15. $-1 = \frac{-y}{4} - 6$

16. $\frac{5x}{6} + 34 = 9$

17. $\frac{-2}{3}d + 3 = 11$

18. $1.2x + 6 = -1.2$

19. $28 = \frac{17}{32}x - 23$

20. $\frac{2x}{5} + 4 = -12$

...More Solving Basic Combined Equations

$$16 - 3(2t - 1) = -11$$
$$16 - 6t + 3 = -11$$
$$19 - 6t = -11$$
$$19 - 19 - 6t = -11 - 19$$
$$\frac{-6t}{-6} = \frac{-30}{-6}$$
$$t = 5$$

1. $y - 16 - 3y = 0$

2. $z - 4 - 4z = -1$

3. $6x - 2x = -64$

4. $8y + 4 - 2y = 22$

5. $12 = 3x - x + 4x$

6. $2(x - 3) - x = -1$

7. $3(y - 4) = 15$

8. $3x - 2(x + 4) = 8$

9. $2(y - 1) - y = -2$

10. $5(2a - 2) + 4 = 4$

11. $3(b + 2) + 2(b - 3) = -5$

12. $4x - 2(x - 5) = -2$

13. $4a - (a + 6) = 12 - 36$

14. $6x - (x + 7) = 13 - 5$

15. $3n + 3(1 - n) - n = -6$

16. $7x - 2(x + 6) = 3$

17. $\frac{6n}{8} + 12 = 84$

18. $-2(-3 - 4x) = -10$

19. $2x + 3(x - 9) - 2(x + 3) = 0$

20. $-6x + 9 + 4x = -3$

Variables and Equations

Solving Equations with Variables on Both Sides

$$4x - 6 = x + 9$$
$$4x - x - 6 = x - x + 9$$
$$3x - 6 = 9$$
$$3x - 6 + 6 = 9 + 6$$
$$\frac{3x}{3} = \frac{15}{3}$$
$$x = 5$$

1. $4x - 6 = x + 9$

2. $4 - 7x = 1 - 6x$

3. $-4x - 3 = -6x + 9$

4. $41 - 2n = 2 + n$

5. $6(2 + y) = 3(3 - y)$

6. $4y = 2(y - 5) - 2$

7. $6x - 9x - 4 = -2x - 2$

8. $-(x + 7) = -6x + 8$

9. $3 - 6a = 9 - 5a$

10. $-9x + 6 = -x + 4$

11. $5x - 7 = -10x + 8$

12. $7y + 3 = 4y - 18$

13. $-3(y + 3) = 2y + 3$

14. $2(-3a + 5) = -4(a + 4)$

15. $7x - 3 = 2(x + 6)$

16. $-6x + 9 = 4(5 - x)$

17. $3(x + 2) = -5 - 2(x - 3)$

18. $2(x - 3) = (x - 1) + 7$

19. $\frac{1}{3}(6y - 9) = -2y + 13$

20. $\frac{1}{6}(12 - 6x) = 5(x + 4)$

Solving Equations: the Big Picture

> ### The Process
>
> 1. Is it a subtraction problem?
>   - (no) (yes)
>   - ↳ Change it to an addition sentence.
> 2. Are there grouping symbols?
>   - (no) (yes)
>   - ↳ Distribute.
> 3. Are there variables on the right side?
>   - (no) (yes)
>   - ↳ Move them to the left side.
>   - combine/simplify left side ↙
> 4. Is there a number *not* attached to the variable?
>   - (no) (yes)
>   - ↳ Move it to the right side (combine).
> 5. Is there a number attached to the variable?
>   - (no) (yes)
>   - ↳ 1. if by $\times$ → then $\div$
>   - 2. if by $\div$ → then $\times$
>   - 3. if a fraction → then use reciprocal
>   - variable = #   ↓
>   - variable = #

Using the chart above solve these problems by asking each question.

1. $3(x - 5) = 21$

2. $x + 9 = 4x - 6$

3. $-6 + 2x = 9 - 3x$

4. $-6x + 9 = -4x - 3$

Equations, the Big Picture...Putting It All Together

1. $\frac{3}{2}x - 9 = 0$

2. $6x + 3 = -5x + 14$

3. $\frac{1}{8}x + 3 = 2$

4. $5y = 2y - 42 - 3y$

5. $37 + 8x = 4(7 - x)$

6. $5(2 - x) = 7x - 26$

7. $6 + 4x = \frac{1}{3}(6x + 9)$

8. $1.6(3y - 1) + 2 = 5y$

9. $7x - 10 = 6(11 - 2x)$

10. $3(4x - 9) = 5(2x - 5)$

11. $\frac{3}{4}(x + 7) = x + 50$

12. $\frac{5}{7}y - 15 = 5y + 30$

Problem Solving Using Equations

Set up and solve each equation.

The sum of twice a number and 21 is 83. Find the number.	$2n + 21 = 83$ $2n + 21 - 21 = 83 - 21$ $2n = 62$ $n = 31$ The number is 31.

1. Twice a number, diminished by 17 is -3. Find the number.

2. Six times a number, increased by 3 is 27. Find the number.

3. Three times the difference of 5 minus a number is 27. Find the number.

4. Karl's team score is 39 points. This was one point less than twice Todd's team score. Find Todd's team score.

5. The length of a rectangle is 6 feet more than twice the width. If the length is 24 feet, what is the width?

6. Four-fifths of the third grade went on a trip to the zoo. If 64 children made the trip, how many children are in the third grade?

7. The price of a pack of gum today is 63¢. This is 3¢ more than three times the price ten years ago. What was the price ten years ago?

8. The sum of three consecutive integers is 279. Find the integers.

9. The sum of two consecutive odd integers is 112. Find the integers.

10. Find four consecutive integers such that the sum of the second and fourth is 132.

11. Find three consecutive odd integers such that their sum decreased by the second equals 50.

...More Problem Solving Using Equations

Set up and solve each equation.

> The sum of two numbers is 52. The difference of the same two numbers is 20. Find the numbers.
>
> x = one number $52 - x$ = second number
>
> $x - (52 - x) = 20$ $52 - x = 52 - 36 = 16$
>
> $x - 52 + x = 20$
>
> $2x - 52 = 20$ The numbers are 36 and 16.
>
> $2x - 52 + 52 = 20 + 52$
>
> $\dfrac{2x}{2} = \dfrac{72}{2}$
>
> $x = 36$

1. One number is four times another. Their sum is 35. Find the numbers.

2. The sum of two numbers is 21. One number is three less than the other. Find the numbers.

3. The greater of two numbers is one less than 8 times the smaller. Their sum is 98. Find the numbers.

4. In a triangle, the second angle measures twice the first, and the third angle measures 5 more than the second. If the sum of the angles' measures is 180°, find the measure of each angle.

5. The length of a rectangle is 4 centimeters (cm) less than three times the width. The perimeter is 64 cm. Find the width and length.
   (Hint: Perimeter = 2l + 2w)

6. The sum of three numbers is 64. The second number is 3 more than the first. The third number is 11 less than twice the first. Find the numbers.

7. Bill can type 19 words per minute faster than Bob. Their combined typing speed is 97 words per minute. Find Bob's typing speed.

Equations and Problem Solving Summary

1. $6y = 10 + 4y$

2. $-27 - 6a = 3a$

3. $10x + 6 = 12x - 18$

4. $8x - (6x - 4) = 10$

5. $3 (x + 5) = 27$

6. $4 (n - 7) = 2n - 8$

7. $3x - (x + 4) = -x + 8$

8. $3 (2y + 4) = 4 (y + 7)$

9. $2 (5x - 3) = 3 (2x + 2)$

10. $4 (a - 5) + 4a = 2 (3a + 4)$

11. One number is 5 more than another. Five times the smaller equals 4 times the larger. Find the numbers.

12. One number is 6 less than another. Three times the smaller is 2 more than twice the larger. Find the numbers.

13. Bill has twice as much money as Bob. Paul has $12 more than Bill. Together they have $92. How much money does Bob have?

14. Find two consecutive whole numbers that total 93.

15. The Colts played 76 games. They won 3 times as many games as they lost. How many did they win?

Basic Inequalities: Solve and Graph

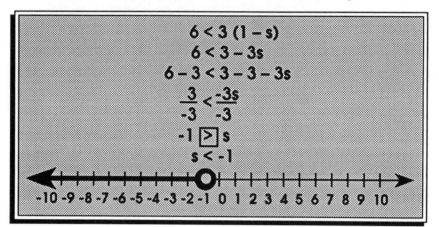

$6 < 3 (1 - s)$

$6 < 3 - 3s$

$6 - 3 < 3 - 3 - 3s$

$\dfrac{3}{-3} < \dfrac{-3s}{-3}$

$-1 \boxed{>} s$

$s < -1$

1. $x + 4 > 12$

2. $32 > -4 (4y)$

3. $3y + 1 < 13$

4. $10\dfrac{1}{2} < 2z + 18\dfrac{1}{2}$

5. $2 - \dfrac{n}{3} < -1$

6. $-2x - 5 > 6$

7. $-3m + 6 (m - 2) > 9$

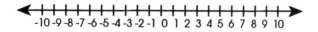

8. $15x - 2 < 3x - 11$

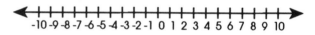

9. $2 (t + 3) < 3 (t + 2)$

10. $15x - 2 (x - 4) > 3$

11. $x - 1.5 < .5 (x + 4)$

12. $-3 (2m - 8) < 2 (m + 14)$

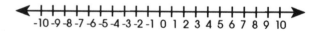

13. $2x + 3 < 6x - 1$

14. $3x - 2 \geq 7x - 10$

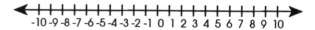

Compound Inequalities: Solve and Graph

$$\frac{2x}{2} \geq \frac{-6}{2}$$

$$x \geq -3$$

$$x > -3 \boxed{\text{ or }} x = -3$$

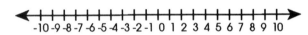

$$3 - 4a \leq 5 \qquad \text{or} \qquad 5a + 1 < -4$$

$$3 - 3 - 4a \leq 5 - 3 \qquad\qquad 5a + 1 - 1 < -4 - 1$$

$$\frac{-4a}{-4} \leq \frac{2}{-4} \qquad\qquad \frac{5a}{5} < \frac{-5}{5}$$

$$a \boxed{\geq} -\frac{1}{2} \qquad \boxed{\text{or}} \qquad a < -1$$

$$2 \leq y + 3 < 6$$

$$2 \leq y + 3 \text{ and } y + 3 < 6$$

$$2 - 3 \leq y + 3 - 3 \qquad\qquad y + 3 - 3 < 6 - 3$$

$$-1 \leq y \qquad\qquad \text{and} \qquad\qquad y < 3$$

$$y \geq -1$$

1. $t \leq -1$ or $t \leq -3$

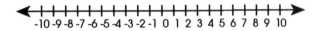

2. $-2 \leq x \leq 6$

3. $x + 1 \leq -3$ or $x + 1 \geq 3$

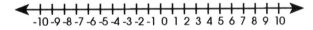

4. $-2 < 3t - 2 < 10$

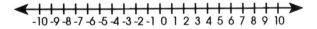

5. $-(x - 2) \geq 3$

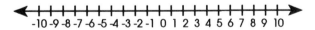

6. $3x - 7 < 11$ or $9x - 4 > x + 4$

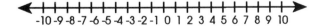

7. $-6 \leq -2z \leq 4$

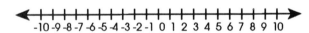

8. $9 \leq 2a + 5 < 15$

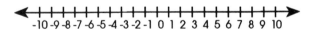

9. $3 < 2x + 1 < 7$

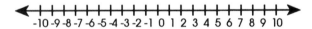

10. $-8 < 2x + 4 \leq -2$

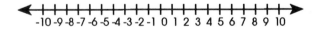

11. $-6 \leq 3 - 2(x + 4) \leq 3$

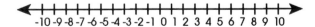

12. $4 - 3x \leq -8$ or $3x - 1 \leq 8$

Keep in mind...
A person who makes no mistakes does not usually make anything.
E. Phelps

Exponents

I. Write in exponential form.

> $4 \cdot x \cdot x \cdot y \cdot y \cdot y = 4x^2y^3$ The cube of $c - 4 = (c - 4)^3$

1. $a \cdot a \cdot a \cdot b$

2. $mn \cdot mn \cdot mn \cdot mn$

3. $9 \cdot x \cdot x \cdot x \cdot x \cdot x \cdot y \cdot y \cdot z$

4. $5(c + 1)(c + 1)(c + 1)$

5. $(a + b)$ squared

6. The quotient of 3 and the cube of $y + 2$

7. $x \cdot x \cdot y \cdot y \cdot y \cdot y \cdot z$

8. $(-x)(-x)(-x)$

9. $3 \cdot ab \cdot ab \cdot ab \cdot ab$

10. The square of $x^2y - 3$

II. Evaluate each expression if $x = -1$, $y = 2$, $z = -3$

> $5x^2z^2 = 5 \cdot x \cdot x \cdot z \cdot z = 5 \cdot -1 \cdot -1 \cdot -3 \cdot -3 = 45$

1. x^5

2. x^2yz

3. $4y^3z$

4. $x^5y^4z^3$

5. $-(xyz)$

6. $10z^5$

7. x^2yz^2

8. $-2xy^2$

9. $\dfrac{x^2z^2}{z}$

10. $11x^2$

Adding and Subtracting Polynomials

$(x^3 + 2x^2 - 8x) - (-2x^2 + 7x - 5) = x^3 + 2x^2 - 8x + 2x^2 - 7x + 5 = x^3 + 4x^2 - 15x + 5$

1. $(4x + 2) + (x - 1)$

2. $(5a - 2b + 4) + (2a + b + 2)$

3. $(3a + 2b) - (a - b)$

4. $(x^2 + y^2 - ab) - (x^2 - y^2 + ab)$

5. $(4a^2 - 5ab - 6b^2) + (10ab - 6a^2 - 8b^2)$

6. $(4x^2 - 2x - 3) - (-5x - 4)$

7. $(4a^2 - 4ab - b^2) + (a^2 - b^2) + (2ab + a^2 + b^2)$

8. $(-4x^3 - 6x^2 + 3x - 1) - (8x^3 + 4x^2 - 2x + 3)$

9. $(a + 2b) + (3b - 4c) + (5a - 7c) + 3b$

10. $(x^2 - 2xy + y^2) - (x^2 - 2xy + y^2)$

11. $(x + 3y) + (-3x - y) - (x - y)$

12. $(2x^2 + 3y^2 - z^2) - (x^2 - y^2 - z^2) + (4x^2 - 3y^2)$

13. $(2x + 3) + (-2x^2 + x - 5)$

14. $(2y + 3x - 4) + (9 - 8y - 5x) + (3x + 4y - 2)$

15. $(-2y^2 + 8) - (3y^2 - 4y - 6)$

16. $(7y + 4x + 9) - (6x - 8y + 11)$

Find the perimeter.

17.

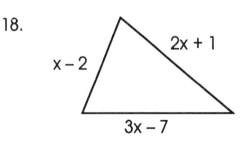

$2x - 6$

$x + 3$ $x + 3$

$2x - 6$

18.

$x - 2$ $2x + 1$

$3x - 7$

Multiplying with Monomials

$$(3a^3b)(5a^2b) = 3 \cdot 5a^{3+2}b^{1+1} = 15a^5b^2$$
$$(-2a^2b)^4 = (-2)^4(a^2)^4(b)^4 = -2 \cdot -2 \cdot -2 \cdot -2a^{2 \cdot 4}b^{1 \cdot 4} = 16a^8b^4$$

1. $(4c)^2$

2. $(2a^2b)(4ab^2)$

3. $(4pq)(-p^2q^3)$

4. $2x(-xy)(-y^2)$

5. $a(2a^2)^3$

6. $3s(-2st)^2$

7. $(-xy^2)^3(2x^2y)^2$

8. $x^2(-2xz)(4z^5)$

9. $(3pq^2r^3)(\frac{1}{3}q^2r)$

10. $(-x)(-2xy)(-3xyz)$

11. $2x^2(xy^2)^2(xz^2)^2$

12. $(2u)^2(u^2v)^3(w)$

13. $(-x)(-x^5)$

14. $(-5x^2)(7xy^3)$

15. $(-x^3y)(6xy^3)(3x^2y^2)$

16. $(-4rt^2)(2rt)(-t^2)$

17. $(-3ab)(-3ab^2)(-3a^2b^3)$

18. $-1(-4x^2)(5x^6)$

Multiply, then add or subtract.

19. $(2a)(3a^3) + (2a^2)(a^2)$

20. $(a^2b)(2a^2b^3) - (a^2b^2)(-3a^2b^2)$

21. $a^2(ab^3)^2 + b^2(a^2b^2)^2$

22. $(r^2s)^3(rs^2)^2 - r(-rs)^7$

Multiplying a Polynomial by a Monomial

$-2a^2 (9 - a - 4a^2) = -2a^2 \cdot 9 - (-2a^2 \cdot a) - (-2a^2 \cdot 4a^2) = -18a^2 + 2a^3 + 8a^4$

$(x + 2) (2x^2) = 2x^2 \cdot x + 2x^2 \cdot 2 = 2x^3 + 4x^2$

1. $2 (x^2 - xy + 3y^2)$

2. $-2n (4 + 5n^3)$

3. $c^2d (c^2d^3 + 2cd^2 + d)$

4. $2xy^2 (2 - x - x^2y)$

5. $(a^2 - 3ab - 2b^2) (-2ab)$

6. $3n (8n^2 - 2n)$

7. $(w^2z - 2wz + z) (-z^2)$

8. $-3ab^2 (a^3b^2 - 2a^2b)$

9. $4x^2y (9x^2 - 6xy^2 - 7)$

10. $-6k^2m^2 (2k - 3m + 4km - k^2m^2)$

11. $-n^2 (n + 4n^2)$

12. $(4x^2 - 7x) (-x)$

13. $2x^2 (x^3 - 2x^2 + 8x - 5)$

14. $(-6x^3) (3x^2 - 1)$

15. $(6x - 5 x^2 + 8) (-3x)$

16. $-5x^2 (2x^3 + 3x^2 - 7x + 9)$

Find the area.

$$A = l \cdot w$$

17.

x + 4

2x

18. A triangle has a base length (b) of 2x + 4 and a height (h) of 3y.

$$\left(\text{Area} = \frac{1}{2} bh\right)$$

Multiplying Polynomials

$$(s - 2)(s^2 - s + 3) = s(s^2 - s + 3) - 2(s^2 - s + 3)$$
$$= s \cdot s^2 - s \cdot s + s \cdot 3 - 2 \cdot s^2 - 2(-s) - 2 \cdot 3$$
$$= s^3 - s^2 + 3s - 2s^2 + 2s - 6$$
$$= s^3 - 3s^2 + 5s - 6$$

1. $(z - 3)(z + 3)$

2. $(3t - 2)(t - 3)$

3. $(a + 5)(a + 5)$

4. $(a + b)(2x + y)$

5. $(\frac{1}{2}x - y)(2x + y)$

6. $(4x - 5)(4x + 5)$

7. $(1.6n - 9)(.2n - 5)$

8. $(2c + d)(c^2 + 2c + 2d)$

9. $(3a^2 - 2b^2)(3a^2 + 2b^2)$

10. $(h + k)(h^2 - 2hk + 3k^2)$

11. $(2x - 1)(x^2 + x + 3)$

12. $(x^3 + 3x^2 + 2x - 1)(x - 1)$

13. $(n - m)(n^2 + m^2)$

14. $(y + 1)(y^2 - 2y + 2)$

15. $(\frac{1}{3}x - 2)(\frac{1}{2}x + 6)$

16. $(3x^2 - 4x - 7)(x + 5)$

17. $(x^2 - 3)(2x^2 + 3x + 5)$

18. $(4x^2 - 6x + 4)(3x + 2)$

26

Multiplying Binomials Using FOIL

$$\underset{2.}{\overset{4.}{(x + 5) \, (x - 3)}} = \underset{\text{First}}{\overset{1.}{x \cdot x}} + \underset{\text{Outer}}{\overset{2.}{x \, (-3)}} + \underset{\text{Inner}}{\overset{3.}{5 \cdot x}} + \underset{\text{Last}}{\overset{4.}{5 \, (-3)}} = x^2 - 3x + 5x - 15 = x^2 + 2x - 15$$

1. $(x + 2) \, (x + 3)$

2. $(y + 7) \, (y + 4)$

3. $(x - 8) \, (x + 4)$

4. $(x - 8) \, (x - 4)$

5. $(y - 4) \, (y + 5)$

6. $(x - 9) \, (x - 2)$

7. $(2x + 4) \, (x + 3)$

8. $(3x + 2) \, (2x + 5)$

9. $(4x - 9) \, (3x + 1)$

10. $(2x + 5) \, (4x - 3)$

11. $(n - 7) \, (3n - 2)$

12. $(5x + 2) \, (3x - 7)$

13. $(-4x + 5) \, (-2x - 3)$

14. $(-x - 4) \, (4 + 3x)$

15. $(x + 2y) \, (2x + 3y)$

16. $(6x - y) \, (3x - 2y)$

17. $(4x + y) \, (3x - 4y)$

18. $(5a + 3b) \, (4a - b)$

...More Multiplying Binomials Using FOIL

$$(x + 3)(x - 4) = x^2 - 4x + 3x - 12 = x^2 - x - 12$$

1. $(n - 7)(n - 2)$

2. $(6 - t)(3 + t)$

3. $(3r + 2)(r - 4)$

4. $(4u - 3)(3u + 2)$

5. $(\frac{1}{2}x + 5)(6x - 10)$

6. $(x + y)(x + 2y)$

7. $(3r + s)(2r - 3s)$

8. $(.3x - .4)(.5x - .1)$

9. $(7m - n)(m - 7n)$

10. $(4b - 3c)(4b + 3c)$

11. $(a^2 - 3b)(a^2 + 2b)$

12. $(8x + \frac{2}{3})(6x + \frac{3}{2})$

13. $(r^2 - 2s)(2r^2 + s)$

14. $(\frac{1}{2}x + 3)(4x + 5)$

15. $(x + 5)(x^2 + 4x)$

16. $(2x^2 - 6x)(7x + 1)$

17. $(2x - 1)(6x - 7)$

18. $(4x - 1)(8x^2 + 3)$

19. $(5x - 2)(-x - 5)$

20. $(x - \frac{1}{2})(2x - \frac{1}{3})$

Special Products

$$(2x + 5)(2x - 5) = 4x^2 - 10x + 10x - 25 = 4x^2 - 25$$

1. $(x + 3)(x - 3)$

2. $(y - 10)(y + 10)$

3. $(a + 4)(a - 4)$

4. $(x + 7)(x - 7)$

5. $(2x + 1)(2x - 1)$

6. $(2x - 3)(2x + 3)$

7. $(5x - 6)(5x + 6)$

8. $(4x + 3)(4x - 3)$

9. $(3x + 3)(3x - 3)$

10. $(3n + 4)(3n - 4)$

11. $(2x + 9)(2x - 9)$

12. $(7x - 5)(7x + 5)$

13. $(x + y)(x - y)$

14. $(5x - y)(5x + y)$

15. $(2x - 5y)(2x + 5y)$

16. $(3x - 7y)(3x + 7y)$

17. $(2x + 11y)(2x - 11y)$

18. $(b - a)(b + a)$

19. $(2x + y^2)(2x - y^2)$

20. $(7n^2 + 8)(7n^2 - 8)$

Squaring Binomials

$$(a + b)^2 = (a + b)(a + b) = a^2 + ab + ab + b^2 = a^2 + 2ab + b^2$$

1. $(x - 8)^2$

2. $(a + 5)^2$

3. $(x - 3)^2$

4. $(3n + 1)^2$

5. $(y - 10)^2$

6. $(3x + 2)^2$

7. $(4x - 3)^2$

8. $(2a + 5)^2$

9. $(6x + 1)^2$

10. $(5b + 2)^2$

11. $(4x - y)^2$

12. $(6x - 5y)^2$

13. $(3y - 5z)^2$

14. $(7a + 2b)^2$

15. $(11x - 2y)^2$

16. $(5a + 3b)^2$

Polynomial Equations

$$2(2x - 1) + 5x = 3(x - 2) + 10$$
$$4x - 2 + 5x = 3x - 6 + 10$$
$$9x - 2 = 3x + 4$$
$$6x - 2 = 4$$
$$6x = 6$$
$$x = 1$$

1. $5(x + 2) - 4(x - 1) = 24$

2. $2(y - 5) - (y + 6) = -4$

3. $2(3n - 1) - (n + 6) = 7$

4. $2(2b + 7) + 2(1 + 2b) = 20$

5. $(4x - 1) - (2x + 2) = x + 5$

6. $2(y + 1) + 3(y - 1) = 9$

7. $(x + 1)(x + 5) = (x + 2)(x + 3)$

8. $-4r + 3(1 - 2r) = 3(5 - 2r)$

9. $(y + 12)(y - 3) = y(y + 5) + 24$

10. $(2x - 3)(2x - 1) = (x - 2)(4x + 3)$

11. $(x - x^2) - (2x^2 + x - 1) = 5 + 2x - 3x^2$

12. $t(t - 2) + 2(2t - 1) = t^2 + 4$

13. $(w + 4)(w + 14) - w(w + 10) = 216$

14. $(2x + 1)^2 - (2x - 1)^2 = (x + 6)^2 - x^2$

Solving Problems with Polynomials

Geometry

Find the perimeter of each polygon.

1.
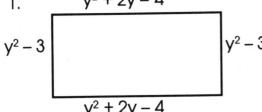

2.
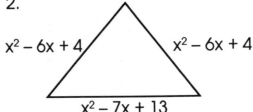

3.
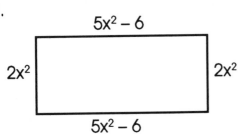

4.
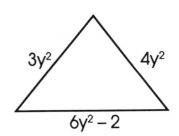

Find the area of each polygon.

5. $A = \frac{1}{2} b \cdot h$
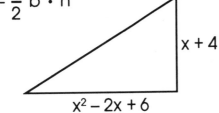

6. $A = s^2$
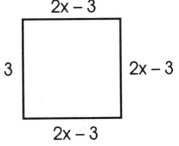

7. $A = l \cdot w$
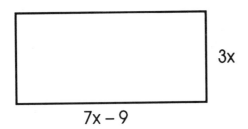

8. $A = s^2$
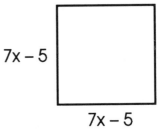

...More Solving Problems with Polynomials

Sally has 21 coins in nickels and dimes. Their total value is $1.75. How many of each coin does she have?

Let x = number of nickels.
21 − x = number of dimes
5x + 10 (21 − x) = 175
value of nickels   value of dimes   total value in cents
5x + 210 − 10x = 175
210 − 5x = 175
-5x = -35
x = 7
There are 7 nickels and 14 dimes.

1. Tim bought some 25¢ and some 29¢ stamps. He paid $7.60 for 28 stamps. How many of each type of stamp did he buy?

2. Tickets for the school concert were $3 and $2. If 245 tickets were sold for a total of $630, how many of each kind were sold?

3. David has 11 coins, some quarters and some dimes. If the coins have a value of $1.55, how many of each kind are there?

4. Subtract $6x^2 - 3xy + y^2$ from $8x^2 + 5xy - y^2$.

5. From $6ab - 2ac + 5bc$, take $10ab - 2bc + 3ac$.

6. Subtract $x^2 - y^2 - z^2$ from the sum of $3x^2 + 2y^2 + z^2$ and $4x^2 + 3y^2 - 5z^2$.

7. Find the perimeter of a rectangle if its length is $(4c + 7)$ units and its width is $(c - 3)$ units.

8. Which has the greater area, a square with sides each $(x + 2)$ units long or a rectangle with length $(x + 4)$ units and width x units?

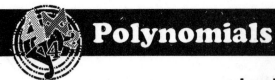

Logic of the Obvious
(Just How Smart Are You?)

We often make mistakes by missing the obvious. Here are some examples. These are not exactly tricky questions. They are rather examples in which the obvious has been overlooked. Our habits and practices lead us to do this often.

1. If it takes 5 minutes to make one cut across a log, how long will it take to cut a 5-foot log into 5 equal pieces?

2. How can two fathers and two sons divide three automobiles among themselves with each receiving one?

3. Some months have 30 days, some have 31. How many have 28 days?

4. If a doctor gave you three pills and told you to take one every half hour, how long would they last?

5. I have two U.S. coins in my hand which total fifty-five cents. One is not a nickel. What are the coins?

6. Two men are playing chess. They played five games and each man won the same number of games with no ties. How is this possible?

7. Why can't a man living in St. Louis be buried in Illinois?

8. If dirt weighs 100 lb. per cubic foot, what is the weight of dirt in a hole three feet square by two feet deep?

9. If you had only one match and entered a dark room in which there was a kerosene lamp, an oil burner and a wood burning stove, which would you light first?

10. Is there a fourth of July in England?

☞ **Keep in mind...**
No one is perfect...that's why pencils have erasers.

I. Greatest Common Factor (GCF)

Find the GCF of the numbers.

$$18, 30$$
$$18 = 2 \cdot 3 \cdot 3$$
$$30 = 2 \cdot 3 \cdot 5$$
$$2 \cdot 3 = 6$$
$$6 = GCF$$

1. 12, 18

2. 10, 35

3. 8, 30

4. 16, 24

5. 28, 49

6. 27, 63

7. 30, 45

8. 48, 72

II. Greatest Common Monomial Factor

Factor, write prime if prime.

$$12a^3b + 15ab^3 = 3ab (4a^2 + 5b^2)$$

1. $6x + 3$

2. $24x^2 - 8x$

3. $6x - 12$

4. $2x^2 + 8x$

5. $4x + 10$

6. $10x^2 + 35x$

7. $10x^2y - 15xy^2$

8. $12x^2 - 9x + 15$

9. $3n^3 - 12n^2 - 30n$

10. $9m^2 - 4n + 12$

11. $2x^3 - 3x^2 + 5x$

12. $13m + 26m^2 - 39m^3$

13. $17x^2 + 34x + 51$

14. $18m^2n^4 - 12m^2n^3 + 24m^2n^2$

Factoring the Difference of Two Squares

$$a^2 - 36 = (a + 6)(a - 6)$$
$$3x^2 - 48 = 3(x^2 - 16) = 3(x + 4)(x - 4)$$

Factor, write prime if prime.

1. $x^2 - 1$

2. $x^2 - 9$

3. $x^2 + 4$

4. $x^2 - 25$

5. $9y^2 - 16$

6. $4x^2 - 25$

7. $9x^2 - 1$

8. $a^2 - x^2$

9. $25 - m^2$

10. $x^2 - 16y^2$

11. $25m^2 - n^2$

12. $-x^2 + 16$

13. $36m^2 - 121$

14. $2x^2 - 8$

15. $25 + 4x^2$

16. $4a^2 - 81b^2$

17. $12x^2 - 75$

18. $a^2b - b^3$

19. $-98 + 2x^2$

20. $5x^2 - 45y^2$

21. $9x^4 - 4$

22. $16x^4 - y^2$

Factoring Perfect Square Trinomials

$$x^2 - 14x + 49 = (x - 7)^2$$

Factor, write prime if prime.

1. $x^2 + 8x + 16$

2. $x^2 - 16x + 64$

3. $y^2 + 12y + 36$

4. $a^2 - 10a + 25$

5. $16y^2 + 8y + 1$

6. $9x^2 - 6x + 1$

7. $25x^2 + 10x + 1$

8. $n^2 - 14n + 49$

9. $81x^2 - 90x + 25$

10. $4y^2 - 20y + 25$

11. $25a^2 + 60a + 36$

12. $16 + 40x + 25x^2$

13. $16x^2 + 24x + 9$

14. $49x^2 - 14x + 1$

15. $9y^2 - 30y + 25$

16. $n^2 + 2n + 4$

17. $b^2 + 2b + 1$

18. $36x^2 + 84x + 49$

19. $81 - 18x + x^2$

20. $4 - 12y + 9y^2$

Special Factoring—Challenge

Factor, write prime if prime.

1. $a^2 - 36$

2. $9x^2 - 49$

3. $169m^2 - 4u^2$

4. $x^2y^2 - 9z^4$

5. $\frac{1}{4}x^2 - 25y^2$

6. $\frac{1}{9}x^2 - 16$

7. $64 - a^4b^4$

8. $y^6 - 100$

9. $\frac{4}{9}x^2y^2 - \frac{25}{36}z^2$

10. $y^8 - 81$

11. $1 - 8u + 16u^2$

12. $a^2b^2 + 6ab + 9$

13. $x^2 + 2xy + y^2$

14. $4x^2 + 12xy + 9y^2$

15. $100h^2 + 20h + 1$

16. $9a^2 - 24a + 16$

17. $4a^3 + 8a^2 + 4a$

18. $5c + 20c^2 + 20c^3$

19. $(x + 4)^2 - (y + 1)^2$

20. $(x - 1)^2 - 10(x - 1) + 25$

Factoring Trinomials: $x^2 + bx + c$

$$x^2 + 7x + 10 = (x)^2 + (2 + 5)x + (2)(5) = (x + 2)(x + 5)$$

Factor, write prime if prime.

1. $x^2 + 6x + 8$

2. $c^2 + 5c + 6$

3. $y^2 - 9y + 14$

4. $x^2 - 10x + 16$

5. $a^2 + 12a + 27$

6. $x^2 - 14x + 24$

7. $x^2 - 15x + 36$

8. $y^2 + 21y + 54$

9. $m^2 + 13m - 36$

10. $x^2 - 8x + 15$

11. $y^2 - 4y - 32$

12. $x^2 - x - 6$

13. $y^2 + 3y - 18$

14. $b^2 + 7b - 18$

15. $a^2 + a - 56$

16. $c^2 - 4c - 12$

17. $x^2 - 9x - 36$

18. $y^2 + 4y - 21$

19. $x^2 - 22x - 75$

20. $x^2 - 3x - 40$

21. $45 + 14y + y^2$

22. $x^2 - 13x + 36$

...More Factoring Trinomials: $x^2 + bx + c$

$$k^2 - k - 20 = (k)^2 + (4 + \text{-}5)\, k + (4)\,(\text{-}5) = (k + 4)\,(k - 5)$$

Factor, write prime if prime.

1. $x^2 + 7x + 12$

2. $m^2 + 10m + 21$

3. $y^2 - 7y - 8$

4. $x^2 - 6x + 5$

5. $x^2 + 4x - 32$

6. $x^2 - 2x - 15$

7. $x^2 - 6x + 8$

8. $y^2 + 9y + 18$

9. $3 - 4t + t^2$

10. $v^2 + 12v + 20$

11. $51 - 20k + k^2$

12. $a^2 - 14ab + 24b^2$

13. $y^2 + 6y - 72$

14. $x^2 - 11xy - 60y^2$

15. $15r^2 + 2rs - s^2$

16. $3x^2 + 21xy - 54y^2$
    (Hint: Check for GCF)

17. $x^2 - 5xy - 6y^2$

18. $x^2 + 8xy + 12y^2$

19. $y^2 - 7xy + 10x^2$

20. $a^2 - 11ab - 60b^2$

Factoring Trinomials: $ax^2 + bx + c$

$$2x^2 - 5x - 3 = (2x + 1)(x - 3)$$

Factor, write prime if prime.

1. $2x^2 - 5x - 3$

2. $3x^2 + 10x - 8$

3. $2y^2 + 15y + 7$

4. $7a^2 - 11a + 4$

5. $5n^2 + 17n + 6$

6. $4y^2 + 8y + 3$

7. $3x^2 + 4x - 7$

8. $2x^2 + 13x + 15$

9. $9y^2 + 6y - 8$

10. $6x^2 - 7x - 20$

11. $2n^2 - 3n - 14$

12. $5n^2 + 2n + 7$

13. $10x^2 + 13x - 30$

14. $12y^2 + 7y + 1$

15. $2n^2 + 9n - 5$

16. $2x^2 + 7x + 6$

17. $5a^2 - 42a - 27$

18. $15x^2 - 28x - 32$

19. $8a^2 - 10a + 3$

20. $2y^2 - 3y - 20$

...More Factoring Trinomials: $ax^2 + bx + c$

Factor, write prime if prime.

1. $3x^2 + 4x + 1$

2. $5z^2 + 7z + 2$

3. $2n^2 - 11n + 5$

4. $3z^2 + z - 2$

5. $5h^2 - 2h - 7$

6. $8s^2 - 10st + 3t^2$

7. $6x^2 + 19x + 15$

8. $28a^2 + 5ab - 12b^2$

9. $2a^2 + 7ab - 15b^2$

10. $12x^2 + 17x + 6$

11. $4a^2 - 4ab - 5b^2$

12. $56y^2 + 15y - 56$

13. $12x^2 - 29xy + 14y^2$

14. $64x^2 + 32y - 21y^2$

15. $16x^2 + 56xy + 49y^2$

16. $18x^2 - 57x + 35$

Factoring: Putting It All Together

$$5x^2 + 20x - 60 = 5(x^2 + 4x - 12) = 5(x + 6)(x - 2)$$

Factor completely, write prime if prime.

1. $2x^2 - 8$

2. $2x^2 + 8x + 6$

3. $3n^2 + 9n - 30$

4. $6x^2 - 26x - 20$

5. $2x^2 + 12x - 80$

6. $5t^2 + 15t + 10$

7. $8n^2 - 18$

8. $14x^2 + 7x - 21$

9. $4x^2 + 16x + 16$

10. $18x + 12x^2 + 2x^3$

11. $2x - 2xy^2$

12. $3t^3 - 27t$

13. $24a^2 - 30a + 9$

14. $10x^2 + 15x - 10$

15. $3x^2 - 42x + 147$

16. $4x^4 - 4x^2$

...More Factoring: Putting It All Together

1. $16x^2 - 40x - 24$

2. $27x^2 - 36x + 12$

3. $5x^2 - 60x - 140$

4. $6m^3 + 54m^2 - 6m$

5. $5k^4 + 8k^3 - 4k^2$

6. $x^2y^4 - x^6$

7. $y^4 - 6y^2 - 16$

8. $x^4 - 3x^2 - 4$

9. $h^2 - (a^2 - 6a + 9)$

10. $81x^4 - 16y^4$

11. $4mn^2 - 4m^2n^2 + m^3n^2$

12. $(2a + 3)^2 - (a - 1)^2$

13. $16d^8 - 8d^4 + 1$

14. $x^2(x^2 - 4) + 4x(x^2 - 4) + 4(x^2 - 4)$

44

Solving Equations Using Factoring

1. Rewrite equation in standard form (one member equals 0).
2. Factor completely.
3. Set each factor equal to 0; then solve.
4. Check results in original equation.

$$x^2 - 7x + 12 = 0$$
$$(x - 4)(x - 3) = 0$$
$$x - 4 = 0 \text{ or } x - 3 = 0$$
$$x = 4 \qquad x = 3$$
$$x = 3, 4$$

$$v^3 = 10v - 3v^2$$
$$v^3 + 3v^2 - 10v = 0$$
$$v(v^2 + 3v - 10) = 0$$
$$v(v + 5)(v - 2) = 0$$
$$v = 0 \text{ or } v + 5 = 0 \text{ or } v - 2 = 0$$
$$v = -5 \qquad v = 2$$
$$v = -5, 0, 2$$

1. $x^2 - 5x - 6 = 0$

2. $v^3 - 4v = 0$

3. $n^2 - 16n = 0$

4. $x^2 + 9 = 10x$

5. $6x^2 = 16x - 8$

6. $s^2 = 56s - s^3$

7. $3y^2 + 2y - 1 = 0$

8. $u^3 = 14u^2 + 32u$

9. $23p = 5p^2 + 24$

10. $x^2 - 3x - 10 = 0$

11. $y^2 = 49$

12. $y^2 = -7y - 10$

13. $x^2 = 8x$

14. $3x^2 - 2 = x^2 + 6$

15. $4y^2 = -4y - 1$

16. $5x^2 - 2x - 3 = 0$

Problem Solving and Factoring

Set up and solve each equation.

> The sum of the squares of two consecutive, positive, even integers is 340. Find the integers.
>
> Let $x = 1^{st}$ integer $\qquad x + 2 = 2^{nd}$ integer
> $$(x)^2 + (x + 2)^2 = 340 \qquad x + 14 = 0 \ \text{or} \ x - 12 = 0$$
> $$x^2 + x^2 + 4x + 4 = 340 \qquad x = -14 \qquad x = 12$$
> $$2x^2 + 4x - 336 = 0 \qquad \qquad \text{rejected}$$
> $$2(x^2 + 2x - 168) = 0$$
> $$2(x + 14)(x - 12) = 0 \qquad \text{The integers are 12 and 14.}$$

1. Fourteen less than the square of a number is the same as five times the number. Find the number.

2. When a number is added to six times its square, the result is 12. Find the number.

3. Find two consecutive, negative integers whose product is 156.

4. The sum of the squares of two consecutive integers is 41. Find the integers.

5. The sum of the squares of three consecutive, positive integers is equal to the sum of the squares of the next two integers. Find the five integers.

6. Find two consecutive even integers whose product is 80.

7. Twice the square of a certain positive number is 144 more than twice the number. What is the number?

8. The square of a positive number decreased by 10 is 2 more than 4 times the number. What is the number?

...More Problem Solving and Factoring

Set up and solve each equation.

> A square field had 9cm added to its length and 3cm added to its width. Its new area is 280cm². Find the length of a side of the original field.
>
> Let x = length of a side of the square field
> $(x + 9)(x + 3) = 280$
> $x^2 + 12x + 27 = 280$
> $x^2 + 12x - 253 = 0$
> $(x + 23)(x - 11) = 0$
> $x + 23 = 0$ or $x - 11 = 0$
> $x = -23$ $x = 11$ The side of the square was
>   rejected   11 cm.

1. The length of a rectangle is 5m greater than twice its width, and its area is 33m². Find the dimensions.

2. The perimeter of a rectanglular piece of property is 8 miles, and its area is 3 square miles. Find the dimensions.
   (Hint: $\frac{1}{2}P = l + w$)

3. When the dimensions of a 2cm X 5cm rectangle were increased by equal amounts, the area was increased by 18cm². Find the dimensions of the new rectangle.

4. If the sides of a square are increased by 3 in., the area becomes 64 in.² Find the length of a side of the original square.

5. A rug placed in a 10 ft X 12 ft room covers two-thirds of the floor area and leaves a uniform strip of bare floor around the edges. Find the dimensions of the rug.

6. The area of a rectangular pool is 192 square meters. The lengh of the pool is 4 meters more than its width. Find the length and width.

Extra: Factoring by Grouping

$$6ax - 2b - 3a + 4bx = 6ax - 3a + 4bx - 2b$$
$$= 3a(2x - 1) + 2b(2x - 1)$$
$$= (2x - 1)(3a + 2b)$$

1. $x^2 + 2x + xy + 2y$

2. $3a^2 - 2b - 6a + ab$

3. $t^3 - t^2 + \underbrace{t - 1}$
   Hint: $t - 1 = 1(t - 1)$

4. $10 + 2t - 5s - st$

5. $\frac{2}{3}bc - \frac{14}{3}b + c - 7$

6. $4u^2 + v + 2uv + 2u$

7. $ad + 3a - d^2 - 3d$

8. $n^2 + 2n + 3mn + 6m$

9. $2ax^2 + bx^2 - 2ay^2 - by^2$

10. $yz^2 - y^3 + z^3 - y^2z$

11. $y^3 - y^2 - 4y + 4$

12. $x^2a + x^2b - 16a - 16b$

13. $x^3 + x^2 - x - 1$

14. $a^3 - a^2 - 8a + 8$

Logic of the Obvious

1. How far can a dog run into the woods?

2. If 30 is divided by $\frac{1}{2}$ and added to 10, what is the answer?

3. Rearrange the letters of NEW DOOR to make one word.

4. In a tennis tournament there are 39 entries. How many matches must be played before there is a champion?

5. A rope ladder is hanging over the side of the ship. Five rungs are below the surface of the water. During the night the tide comes in and the water rises at the rate of 16 inches an hour. How many rungs will be in the water after 3 hours?

6. How many birthdays does the average man have?

7. A man builds a house with four sides to it, a rectangular structure. Each side has a southern exposure. A big bear comes wandering by. What color is the bear?

8. How many men are on a baseball team? How many outs in each inning?

9. Is it legal in North Carolina for a man to marry his widow's sister?

10. What do you have if you take 2 apples from 5 apples?

Algebraic Fractions

 Keep in mind...
The dictionary is the only place where success comes before work.

Dividing Monomials

$$\frac{18x^6y}{-3x^3y^5} = \frac{18}{-3} \cdot \frac{x^{6-3}}{1} \cdot \frac{1}{y^{5-1}} = \frac{-6x^3}{y^4}$$

1. $\dfrac{m^{10}}{m^5}$

2. $\dfrac{x^3y^2}{2x^2y^2}$

3. $\dfrac{4ab^3}{2a^2b^2}$

4. $\dfrac{27u^2v^3}{-18u^4v^5}$

5. $\dfrac{13c^9d^{10}}{-26c^9d}$

6. $\dfrac{3s^5t^7}{-3s^5t^7}$

7. $\dfrac{-52x^3y^2z}{13xy^2}$

8. $\dfrac{8xy^2}{16x^3y^5}$

9. $\dfrac{5x^4}{5}$

10. $\dfrac{18x^2y}{24xy}$

11. $\dfrac{56s^2t^3}{4s^2t}$

12. $\dfrac{48a^3bc^5}{12a^5b^3c^2}$

13. $\dfrac{25x^2y}{-15xy^2}$

14. $\dfrac{8m^2n^2}{12m^2n^3}$

15. $\dfrac{-17c^5d^4}{-51cd^3}$

16. $\dfrac{24x^2y^3z^4}{-44x^4y^3z^2}$

Dividing a Polynomial by a Monomial

$$\frac{r^2 + 6r + 5}{r} = \frac{r^2}{r} + \frac{6r}{r} + \frac{5}{r}$$

$$= r + 6 + \frac{5}{r}$$

1. $\dfrac{a^2 + 2a}{a}$

2. $\dfrac{14x + 35}{7}$

3. $\dfrac{4y^2 + 6y}{2y}$

4. $\dfrac{x^2y - xy^2}{xy}$

5. $\dfrac{25u^2 - 15u - 5}{-5}$

6. $\dfrac{12x^2 - 9x^3 + 6x^4}{3x}$

7. $\dfrac{m^2n^2 + m - n}{mn}$

8. $\dfrac{45a^2b^4 - 60a^3b^2 - 15a^2b}{-15a^2b}$

9. $\dfrac{14k^9m^3 - 4k^2m^2 + 12km^3}{2km^2}$

10. $\dfrac{12v^5 - 27v^4 + 18uv^3}{3uv^3}$

11. $\dfrac{2x^2 - 10xy}{2x}$

12. $\dfrac{3x^3y^2 - 6x^2y^2 + 6xy^2}{3xy}$

13. $\dfrac{6z^2 - 3z + 9}{3z}$

14. $\dfrac{6a^2 + 42a + 72}{6a^3}$

15. $\dfrac{64x^4 - 64x^3}{64x^3}$

16. $\dfrac{18m^3n^4 - 12m^2n^3 + 24n^2}{6m^2n}$

Algebraic Fractions

Simplifying Fractions

$$\frac{5x^2 + 30x - 35}{5 - 5x^2} = \frac{\cancel{5}\,(x + 7)\,\cancel{(x - 1)}}{-\cancel{5}\,(x + 1)\,\cancel{(x - 1)}}$$

$$= -\frac{x + 7}{x + 1}$$

1. $\dfrac{8a - 8b}{a^2 - b^2}$

2. $\dfrac{x^2 + 8x + 16}{x^2 - 16}$

3. $\dfrac{12 - 4a}{a^2 + a - 12}$

4. $\dfrac{t^2 + 4t - 5}{t^2 + 9t + 20}$

5. $\dfrac{z^2 - 4z - 5}{z^2 + 4z - 45}$

6. $\dfrac{6b^3 - 24b^2}{b^2 + b - 20}$

7. $\dfrac{-x^2 + 8x - 12}{x - 2}$

8. $\dfrac{2a^3 + a^2 - 3a}{6a^3 + 5a^2 - 6a}$

9. $\dfrac{x^2 - 9}{x^2 + x - 6}$

10. $\dfrac{3x^2 + 2x - 1}{x^2 + 3x + 2}$

11. $\dfrac{x^2 + 5x}{x^2 - 25}$

12. $\dfrac{a^2 - 11a + 30}{a^2 - 9a + 18}$

13. $\dfrac{2y^3 - 12y^2 + 2y}{y^2 - 6y + 1}$

14. $\dfrac{a + b}{a^2 + 2ab + b^2}$

Multiplying Fractions

$$\frac{-22cd^2}{2d} \cdot \frac{17c^2d}{17d} = \frac{-1 \cdot \cancel{2} \cdot 11 \cdot c\cancel{d}^{\,d}}{\cancel{2d}} \cdot \frac{\cancel{17}c^2d}{\cancel{17d}}$$

$$= -11c^3d$$

$$\frac{3x-6}{6x+6} \cdot \frac{x^2+3x+2}{x^2-3x+2} = \frac{\cancel{3}\,(x-2)}{\cancel{6}\,(x+1)} \cdot \frac{(x+2)\,(x+1)}{(x-2)\,(x-1)}$$

$$= \frac{x+2}{2\,(x-1)}$$

1. $\dfrac{24r^2s^2}{3s} \cdot \dfrac{-21s}{r}$

2. $\dfrac{x^2y}{z^2} \cdot \dfrac{z}{xy}$

3. $\dfrac{2t+16}{4t} \cdot \dfrac{10t^2}{3t+24}$

4. $\dfrac{x^2-1}{x} \cdot \dfrac{x^2}{x-1}$

5. $\dfrac{a+b}{a-b} \cdot \dfrac{a^2-b^2}{a+b}$

6. $\dfrac{a^2-4}{a^2-1} \cdot \dfrac{a-1}{a-1}$

7. $\dfrac{2x+2}{x-1} \cdot \dfrac{x^2+x-2}{x^2-x-2}$

8. $\dfrac{z^2-6z-7}{z^2+z} \cdot \dfrac{z^2-z}{3z-21}$

9. $\dfrac{c^2-6c-16}{c^2+4c-21} \cdot \dfrac{c^2-8c+15}{c^2+9c+14}$

10. $\dfrac{x+8}{x^2-x-12} \cdot \dfrac{x^2-6x+8}{x^2+6x-16}$

11. $\dfrac{h^2-2h-3}{h^2-9} \cdot \dfrac{h^2+5h+6}{h^2-1}$

12. $\dfrac{x^2-y^2}{x^2+4xy+3y^2} \cdot \dfrac{x^2+xy-6y^2}{x^2+xy-2y^2}$

13. $\dfrac{30+y-y^2}{25-y^2} \cdot \dfrac{y^2}{y^2-6y} \cdot \dfrac{y^2-y-12}{y^2-9}$

14. $\dfrac{5m+5n}{m^2-n^2} \cdot \dfrac{m^2-mn}{(m+n)^2}$

Dividing Fractions

$$\frac{12a^2b^2}{21xy^2} \div \frac{4ab^2}{7y^2} = \frac{12a^2b^2}{21xy^2} \cdot \frac{7y^2}{4ab^2}$$

$$= \frac{a}{x}$$

1. $\dfrac{b+2}{b^2-9} \div \dfrac{1}{b-3}$

2. $\dfrac{c^2+2cd}{2cd+d^2} \div \dfrac{c^3+2c^2d}{cd+d^2}$

3. $\dfrac{x^2+3x^3}{4-x^2} \div \dfrac{x+4x^2+3x^3}{2x+x^2}$

4. $\dfrac{a^2-a-20}{a^2+7a+12} \div \dfrac{a^2-7a+10}{a^2+9a+18}$

5. $\dfrac{6a^2-a-2}{12a^2+5a-2} \div \dfrac{4a^2-1}{8a^2-6a+1}$

6. $\dfrac{a^3-6a^2+8a}{5a} \div \dfrac{2a-4}{10a-40}$

7. $\dfrac{12x+36}{x^2-2x-8} \div \dfrac{15x+45}{x^2+x-20}$

8. $\dfrac{x^2-y^2}{x^2+2xy+y^2} \div \dfrac{x-y}{x+y}$

9. $(y^2-9) \div \dfrac{y^2+8y+15}{2y+10}$

10. $\dfrac{x^2-4x+4}{3x-6} \div (x-2)$

11. $\dfrac{(2a)^3}{(4bc)^3} \div \dfrac{16a^2}{8b^2c^3}$

12. $\dfrac{\dfrac{26c^2}{5c^2d}}{\dfrac{13c^3}{25d^3}}$

Combination Problems

Express answers in simplest form.

1. $\dfrac{6x}{3x - 7} \cdot \dfrac{9x - 21}{21} \div \dfrac{x^2}{35}$

2. $\dfrac{x^2 - x - 6}{x^2 + 2x - 15} \cdot \dfrac{x^2 - 25}{x^2 - 4x - 5} \div \dfrac{x^2 + 5x + 6}{x^2 - 1}$

3. $\dfrac{x - y}{x + y} \div \dfrac{5x^2 - 5y^2}{3x - 3y} \cdot \dfrac{(x + y)^2}{x^2 - y^2}$

4. $(b^2 - 9) \div \dfrac{b^2 + 8b + 15}{2b + 10} \div (b - 3)$

5. $\dfrac{a^3b^3}{a^3 - ab^2} \div \dfrac{abc}{a - b} \cdot \dfrac{ab + bc}{ab}$

6. $\dfrac{x^2 + 16x + 64}{x^2 - 9} \div \dfrac{x^2 - 64}{x + 3} \cdot (x^2 - 11x + 24)$

Adding and Subtracting Fractions with Like Denominators

$$\frac{5}{17} + \frac{3}{17} - \frac{11}{17} = \frac{5 + 3 - 11}{17}$$
$$= \frac{-3}{17}$$

$$\frac{5a + 3c}{2a} - \frac{a - c}{2a} = \frac{5a + 3c - (a - c)}{2a}$$
$$= \frac{5a + 3c - a + c}{2a}$$
$$= \frac{4a + 4c}{2a}$$
$$= \frac{2 \cdot 2 (a + c)}{2a}$$
$$= \frac{2 (a + c)}{a}$$

1. $\dfrac{2}{x} - \dfrac{8}{x} + \dfrac{3}{x}$

2. $\dfrac{3a}{5b} + \dfrac{2a}{5b}$

3. $\dfrac{r}{6} - \dfrac{5t}{6}$

4. $\dfrac{x + y}{2} - \dfrac{x}{2}$

5. $\dfrac{c}{c - d} - \dfrac{d}{c - d}$

6. $\dfrac{6a}{a + d} + \dfrac{6d}{a + d}$

7. $\dfrac{x^2}{x - 2} - \dfrac{4}{x - 2}$

8. $\dfrac{c^2}{c^2 - 4} - \dfrac{6c + 16}{c^2 - 4}$

9. $\dfrac{x^2 - 7x}{(x - 3)^2} + \dfrac{12}{(x - 3)^2}$

10. $\dfrac{x^2}{2x + 14} - \dfrac{49}{2x + 14}$

11. $\dfrac{7x}{2y + 5} - \dfrac{6x}{2y + 5}$

12. $\dfrac{y + 4}{y - 5} - \dfrac{3y + 1}{y - 5}$

13. $\dfrac{2x - 3}{2} - \dfrac{6x - 5}{2}$

14. $\dfrac{8a - 1}{5} - \dfrac{3a - 6}{5}$

Adding and Subtracting Fractions with Unlike Denominators

$$\frac{1}{7} - \frac{a}{b} = \frac{1 \cdot b}{7 \cdot b} - \frac{7 \cdot a}{7 \cdot b}$$

$$= \frac{b}{7b} - \frac{7a}{7b}$$

$$= \frac{b - 7a}{7b}$$

$$\frac{3}{x^2} + \frac{5}{2xy} - \frac{4}{3y^2} = \frac{3 \cdot 6y^2}{x^2 \cdot 6y^2} + \frac{5 \cdot 3xy}{2xy \cdot 3xy} - \frac{4 \cdot 2x^2}{3y^2 \cdot 2x^2}$$

$$= \frac{18y^2 + 15xy - 8x^2}{6x^2y^2}$$

1. $\dfrac{1}{x} + \dfrac{1}{y}$

2. $\dfrac{3n}{7} + \dfrac{n}{14}$

3. $\dfrac{2x}{3} + \dfrac{5y}{2}$

4. $\dfrac{x}{3} + \dfrac{x^2}{5}$

5. $\dfrac{2x}{x^2y} - \dfrac{y}{xy^2}$

6. $\dfrac{5}{12xy} + \dfrac{3}{4x}$

7. $\dfrac{a}{b} - \dfrac{c}{d}$

8. $\dfrac{8}{x} + \dfrac{3}{xy}$

9. $\dfrac{4x - 1}{3x} + \dfrac{x - 8}{5x}$

10. $\dfrac{2x + 1}{4} - \dfrac{x - 1}{8}$

11. $\dfrac{a + 2b}{3} + \dfrac{a + b}{2}$

12. $\dfrac{1}{x} + \dfrac{2}{x^2} - \dfrac{3}{x^3}$

Algebraic Fractions

...More Adding and Subtracting Fractions with Unlike Denominators

$$\frac{x+1}{x^2-9} + \frac{4}{x+3} - \frac{x-1}{x-3} = \frac{x+1}{(x+3)(x-3)} + \frac{4(x-3)}{(x+3)(x-3)} - \frac{(x-1)(x+3)}{(x-3)(x+3)}$$

$$= \frac{x+1+4x-12-(x^2+2x-3)}{(x+3)(x-3)}$$

$$= \frac{5x-11-x^2-2x+3}{(x+3)(x-3)}$$

$$= \frac{-x^2+3x-8}{x^2-9}$$

1. $\dfrac{3a+2b}{3b} - \dfrac{a+2b}{6a}$

2. $\dfrac{a}{2a+2b} - \dfrac{b}{3a+3b}$

3. $\dfrac{3x}{2y-3} + \dfrac{2x}{3-2y}$

   Hint: $3-2y = -1(2y-3)$

4. $\dfrac{x}{x+3} + \dfrac{9x+18}{x^2+3x}$

5. $\dfrac{x+3}{x-5} + \dfrac{x-5}{x+3}$

6. $\dfrac{11x}{x^2+3x-28} + \dfrac{x}{x+7}$

7. $\dfrac{d^2+3}{d^2-2d} - \dfrac{d-4}{d}$

8. $\dfrac{4a}{2a+6} - \dfrac{a-1}{a+3}$

9. $\dfrac{a+b}{ax+ay} - \dfrac{a+b}{bx+by}$

10. $\dfrac{8}{c^2-4} + \dfrac{2}{c^2-5c+6}$

11. $\dfrac{x}{x^2-16} + \dfrac{6}{4-x} - \dfrac{1}{x-4}$

12. $\dfrac{1}{a^2-a-2} + \dfrac{1}{a^2+2a+1}$

13. $\dfrac{5}{3x-3} + \dfrac{x}{2x+2} - \dfrac{3x^2}{x^2-1}$

14. $\dfrac{x+1}{x^2-9} + \dfrac{4}{x+3} - \dfrac{x-1}{x-3}$

Simplifying Mixed Expressions

$$\frac{a}{x+3} + \frac{a}{x-3} - 2 = \frac{a(x-3)}{(x+3)(x-3)} + \frac{a(x+3)}{(x+3)(x-3)} - \frac{2(x+3)(x-3)}{(x+3)(x-3)}$$

$$= \frac{ax - 3a + ax + 3a - 2x^2 + 18}{(x+3)(x-3)}$$

$$= \frac{2ax - 2x^2 + 18}{x^2 - 9}$$

1. $b + \dfrac{6}{b-1}$

2. $3 + \dfrac{a+2b}{a-b}$

3. $x - y + \dfrac{1}{x+y}$

4. $7 + \dfrac{3}{a} + \dfrac{6}{b}$

5. $\dfrac{5}{x+2} + 1$

6. $d + 3 + \dfrac{2d-1}{d-2}$

7. $\dfrac{2x-3}{x+2} - 4$

8. $2x - \dfrac{x+y}{y}$

9. $\dfrac{8}{3a-1} - 6$

10. $(x-4) - \dfrac{1}{x-2}$

11. $\dfrac{x}{2y} - (x+2)$

12. $(a+2) + \dfrac{7}{a-2}$

13. $4 - \dfrac{3}{y-1} - \dfrac{1}{y+1}$

14. $\dfrac{\dfrac{a}{b} + 1}{\dfrac{a}{b} - 1}$

Algebraic Fractions

Dividing Polynomials

$$\frac{6a2 + 4a + 3}{3a - 1} \Rightarrow 3a - 1 \overline{\smash{\big)}\ \begin{array}{c} 2a + 2 + \dfrac{5}{3a - 1} \\ \hline 6a^2 + 4a + 3 \\ \underline{6a^2 - 2a} \\ 6a + 3 \\ \underline{6a - 2} \\ 5 \end{array}}$$

1. $\dfrac{s^2 + 3s - 4}{4 + s}$

    (Hint: Rewrite denominator as s + 4)

2. $\dfrac{a^2 + 2a + 3}{a + 3}$

3. $\dfrac{x^2 + 4}{x + 2}$

    (Hint: Write dividend as $x^2 + 0x + 4$)

4. $\dfrac{3c^2 + 8c + 4}{3c + 2}$

5. $\dfrac{6r^2 + r - 5}{2r - 3}$

6. $\dfrac{9t^2 + 1}{3t + 2}$

7. $\dfrac{2u^2 - 3uv - 9v^2}{u - 3v}$

8. $\dfrac{z^3 + z^2 - 3z + 9}{z + 3}$

9. $\dfrac{6x^3 + 5x^2 + 9}{2x + 3}$

10. $\dfrac{2y^3 + 5y^2 + 7y + 6}{y^2 + y + 2}$

11. $x^3 - x^2 - 2x + 10 \div x + 2$

12. $8x + 13x^2 + 6x^3 + 5 \div 3x + 5$

13. $y^3 - 2y^2 + 3 \div y + 1$

14. $\dfrac{-32x + 2x^3 + 42}{2x - 6}$

Synthetic Division

$$\frac{x^2 - 5x - 24}{x + 3} \implies$$

$$
\begin{array}{r|rrr}
-3 & 1 & -5 & -24 \\
   &   & -3 & 24 \\
\hline
   & 1 & -8 & 0
\end{array}
$$

$$= x - 8$$

1. $y^2 - 13y + 36 \div y - 4$

   Hint:
   $$
   \begin{array}{r|rrr}
   4 & 1 & -13 & 36 \\
   \hline
   \end{array}
   $$

2. $x^2 + 10x + 21 \div x + 3$

3. $4a^2 + 19a + 21 \div a + 1$

4. $x^3 - 5x^2 + 2x + 8 \div x - 2$

5. $y^2 + 25 \div y + 5$

6. $x^3 + 2x^2 - 2x + 24 \div x + 4$

Ratios

I. Express each ratio as a fraction in simplest form.

> 45 seconds to 3 minutes
>
> $$\frac{45}{3 \cdot 60} = \frac{45 \text{ sec}}{180 \text{ sec}} = \frac{1}{4}$$
>
> The ratio of males to total students in a school with 1200 males and 1000 females.
>
> $$\frac{1200}{1000 + 1200} = \frac{1200 \text{ males}}{2200 \text{ students}} = \frac{6}{11}$$

1. 55¢ to $4

2. 10 inches to 1 yard

3. 8 hours to 3 days

4. The ratio of wins to losses in 35 games with 21 losses and no ties.

5. The ratio of the area of a rectangle with sides of 6m and 8m to the area of a square with sides of length 12m.

6. The ratio of girls to boys in a class of 40 students with 17 girls.

7. Big Bob's batting average if he had 3 hits in 4 at bats against the Cougars.

8. The ratio of wins to losses in 42 games with 35 wins and no ties.

II. Set up and solve each of the following.

> Find two numbers in the ratio of 4:3 whose sum is 63.
>
> Let x = common factor $\quad$ 4x + 3x = 63 $\quad$ 4 · 9 = 36
> 4x = first number $\quad\quad$ 7x = 63 $\quad\quad$ 3 · 9 = 27
> 3x = second number $\quad$ x = 9 $\quad\quad$ The numbers are 36 and 27.

9. A 36 cm segment is divided into three parts whose lengths have the ratio of 2:3:7. Find the length of each segment.

10. The sum of the measures of two complementary angles is 90°. Find the measures of two complementary angles whose measures are in the ratio of 1:4.

Proportions

$$\frac{x}{12} = \frac{5}{3}$$

A pipe delivers 5 gallons of water in 45 seconds. How much will it deliver in 15 minutes?

$3x = 12 \cdot 5$

$3x = 60$

$x = 20$

$$\frac{5 \text{ gal}}{45 \text{ sec}} = \frac{x \text{ gal}}{15 \cdot 60 \text{ sec}}$$

$45x = 5 \cdot 900$

$45x = 4500$

$x = 100$ **100 gallons**

1. $\dfrac{9}{11} = \dfrac{16}{x}$

2. $\dfrac{5}{13} = \dfrac{a}{65}$

3. $\dfrac{y}{2.5} = \dfrac{21}{5}$

4. $\dfrac{z-8}{21} = \dfrac{1}{3}$

5. $\dfrac{2x+1}{3} = \dfrac{4}{5}$

6. $\dfrac{n}{16-n} = \dfrac{5}{3}$

7. $\dfrac{2x+1}{9} = \dfrac{x}{4}$

8. $\dfrac{3m}{m+4} = \dfrac{5}{3}$

9. $\dfrac{x-2}{x} = \dfrac{x-1}{x+2}$

10. If 30m of wire weigh 8 kilograms, what will 40m of the same kind of wire weigh?

11. On a map, $1\frac{1}{2}$ cm represents 60 km. What distance does 6 cm represent?

12. A post casts a shadow 9 feet long. A girl 5 feet tall casts a shadow 15 feet long at the same time and place. How tall is the pole?

13. If Marilyn drove 270 miles in $4\frac{1}{2}$ hours, how far would she travel in 7 hours?

14. The sales tax on an $800 purchase is $24. At this rate, what is the tax on a $600 purchase?

Percents

Find 25% of $240.
$$\frac{25}{100} = \frac{x}{240}$$
$$100x = 25 \cdot 240$$
$$100x = 6000$$
$$x = \$60$$

If 20% of a number is 32, find the number.
$$\frac{20}{100} = \frac{32}{x}$$
$$20x = 32 \cdot 100$$
$$20x = 3200$$
$$x = 160$$
The number is 160.

What percent is 15 out of 45?
$$\frac{x}{100} = \frac{15}{45}$$
$$45x = 100 \cdot 15$$
$$45x = 1500$$
$$x = 33\frac{1}{3}$$
$$33\frac{1}{3}\%$$

1. 72% of 310

2. 21 is 35% of what number?

3. 28 out of 70 is what percent?

4. 6% of what number is 2.36?

5. 3.9 is what percent of 10?

6. 115% of 12

7. 60% of what number is 54?

8. 17% of 800 is what number?

9. What percent of 72 is 27?

10. A piece of jewelry costs $78. If the price increases by 12%, what is the new cost?

11. Tax on a $24 item is $1.56. What is the tax rate (percent)?

12. A dress was reduced in price by $19.56. This was 20% of the original price. Find the sale price.

13. There are 252 students on the student council at West High School. If there are 700 students enrolled, what percent are on the student council?

14. One day 3% of the sweatshirts made at a factory were defective. 15 sweatshirts were defective. How many sweatshirts were produced at the factory that day?

Solving Fractional Equations

$$\frac{2}{3x} + \frac{1}{2} = \frac{3}{4x}$$

$$12x \cdot \frac{2}{3x} + 12x \cdot \frac{1}{2} = 12x \cdot \frac{3}{4x}$$

$$8 + 6x = 9$$

$$6x = 1$$

$$x = \frac{1}{6}$$

1. $\dfrac{5}{6x} + 3 = \dfrac{1}{2x}$

2. $\dfrac{2}{5n} = \dfrac{3}{10n} - \dfrac{3}{5}$

3. $\dfrac{4}{3x} - \dfrac{5}{2x} = 5 + \dfrac{1}{6x}$

4. $\dfrac{c-7}{c+2} = \dfrac{1}{4}$

5. $\dfrac{y}{y-3} = 2$

6. $\dfrac{2x}{5} + \dfrac{1}{2} = \dfrac{3x}{10}$

7. $\dfrac{x}{x-2} = \dfrac{4}{5}$

8. $\dfrac{2}{3} = \dfrac{y}{y+3}$

9. $\dfrac{10}{x-3} = \dfrac{9}{x-5}$

10. $\dfrac{7}{x} - \dfrac{4x}{2x-3} = -2$

11. $\dfrac{3}{x} + \dfrac{1}{2x} = \dfrac{7}{8}$

12. $\dfrac{3}{4} = \dfrac{x+5}{x-2}$

Algebraic Fractions

...More Solving Fractional Equations

$$\frac{2}{x^2 - x} - \frac{2}{x - 1} = 1$$

$$x(x-1) \cdot \frac{2}{x(x-1)} - x(x-1)\frac{2}{x-1} = x(x-1) \cdot 1$$

$$2 - 2x = x^2 - x$$
$$0 = x^2 + x - 2$$
$$0 = (x + 2)(x - 1)$$

$$x + 2 = 0 \qquad x - 1 = 0 \quad \text{1 is rejected because}$$
$$x = -2 \qquad x = 1 \quad \text{denominator} \neq 0.$$

1. $\dfrac{1}{u + 4} + \dfrac{1}{u - 4} = \dfrac{6}{u^2 - 16}$

2. $\dfrac{x}{8} + \dfrac{1}{x - 2} = \dfrac{x + 2}{2x - 4}$

3. $\dfrac{5y}{y + 1} - \dfrac{y}{y + 6} = 4$

4. $\dfrac{d}{d - 2} = \dfrac{d + 3}{d + 2} - \dfrac{d}{d^2 - 4}$

5. $\dfrac{6y}{2y + 1} - \dfrac{3}{y} = -1$

6. $2 + \dfrac{4}{b - 1} = \dfrac{4}{b^2 - b}$

7. $\dfrac{2z^2 + z - 3}{z^2 + 1} = 2$

8. $\dfrac{x}{x - 3} + \dfrac{2}{x + 4} = 1$

9. $\dfrac{1}{m - 3} + \dfrac{1}{m + 5} = \dfrac{m + 1}{m - 3}$

10. $\dfrac{c}{c + 1} + \dfrac{3}{c - 3} + 1 = 0$

11. $\dfrac{b}{b + 1} - \dfrac{b + 1}{b - 4} = \dfrac{5}{b^2 - 3b - 4}$

12. $\dfrac{2}{2y + 1} - \dfrac{1}{2y} = \dfrac{3}{2y + 1}$

Problem Solving: Mixture Problems

> How much water must be added to 20kg of
> a 10% salt solution to produce a 5% solution?
> Let x = amount of water
> 10% · 20 + 0%x = 5% · (x + 20)
> 2 + 0 = .05x + 1
> 1 = .05x
> 20 = x   20 kg of water

1. How much water must be added to 60kg of an 80% acid solution to produce a 50% solution?

2. How much water must be evaporated from 8 grams of a 30% antiseptic solution to produce a 40% solution?

3. How many grams of alcohol must be added to 40 grams of a 15% alcohol solution to obtain a 20% alcohol solution?

4. How many quarts of antifreeze must be added to 15 quarts of a 30% antifreeze solution to obtain a 50% antifreeze solution?

5. A candy mixture is created with 2 types of candy, one costing $4 per pound and the other $3.50 per pound. How much of each type is needed for a 5 pound box that costs $18?

6. A seed company mixes two types of seed for bird feeding. One costs $1.10 per kg and the other costs $2.25 per kg. How much of each type of seed is needed to produce 6 kg at a cost of $8.90?

7. A farmer wants to mix milk containing 6% butterfat with 2 quarts of cream that is 15% butterfat to obtain a mixture that is 12% butterfat. How much milk containing 6% butterfat must he use?

8. A store owner has 12 pounds of pasta worth 70¢ a pound. She wants to mix it with pasta worth 45¢ a pound so that the total mixture can be sold for 55¢ a pound (without any gain or loss). How much of the 45¢ pasta must she use?

Problem Solving: Simple Interest and Percent Problems

If $1400 is added to an account earning 6% annually, the interest will amount to $192. How much was in the account originally?

Let x = original account

$$.06 (x + 1400) = \$192$$
$$.06x + 84 = 192$$
$$.06x = 108$$
$$x = 1800 \quad \text{account had } \$1800$$

1. How much interest can be earned in one year on $800 at 6%?

2. How long will it take $1000 to double at 6% interest?

3. Sam invested $1600, part at 5% and the rest at 6%. The money earned $85 in one year. How much was invested at 5%?

   Hint:

	P	x r	x t	= I
Amount at 5%	x		1	
Amount at 6%	1600 – x		1	

4. The Lewis family invested $900, part at 5% and the rest at 7%. the income from the investment was $58. How much was invested at 7%?

5. The Lockmores invested $7000, part at 8% and part at $6\frac{1}{2}$%. If the annual return was $537.50, how much was invested at each rate?

6. BDLV Associates had $7400 invested at $5\frac{1}{2}$%. After money was withdrawn, $242 was earned on the remaining funds. How much money was withdrawn?

7. Michael has $2000 more invested at $8\frac{1}{2}$ % than he does at $9\frac{3}{4}$ %. If the annual return from each investment is the same, how much is invested at each rate?

8. Ms. Burke invested $53,650, part at 10.5% and the rest at 12%. If the income from the 10.5% investment is one third of that from the 12% investment, how much did she invest at each rate?

Problem Solving: Work Problems

Anne can complete a project in 6 hours. It takes Will 9 hours to do the same job. How long will it take them if they work together?

Let x = number of hours for both to complete job $\quad \frac{1}{6} \cdot x + \frac{1}{9} \cdot x = 1$

$\frac{1}{6}$ = Anne's rate $\qquad\qquad\qquad\qquad\qquad\qquad\qquad\qquad \frac{x}{6} + \frac{x}{9} = 1$

$\frac{1}{9}$ = Will's rate $\qquad\qquad\qquad\qquad\qquad 18 \cdot \frac{x}{6} + 18 \cdot \frac{x}{9} = 18 \cdot 1$

$\qquad\qquad\qquad\qquad\qquad\qquad\qquad\qquad\qquad\qquad 3x + 2x = 18$

$\qquad\qquad\qquad\qquad\qquad\qquad\qquad\qquad\qquad\qquad\qquad 5x = 18$

$\qquad\qquad\qquad\qquad\qquad\qquad\qquad\qquad\qquad\qquad x = \frac{18}{5} \text{ or } 3\frac{3}{5}$

They can complete the project in $3\frac{3}{5}$ hours.

1. Bill can paint a closet in 2 hours. Bob can paint the same closet in 3 hours. How long will it take them to paint the closet working together?

2. Sally can address a box of envelopes in 30 minutes. Her brother Jim can address a box of envelopes in 1 hour. How long would it take both working together to address a box of envelopes?

3. Paul can mow the grass in 50 minutes but it takes Dan three times as long. How long will it take them to mow the grass if they work together?

4. Using 1 drain, a swimming pool can be emptied in 45 minutes. Using a different drain, the job requires 1 hour and 15 minutes. How long will it take if both drains are opened?

5. Susan can sort the office mail in 15 minutes but if Kathy helps, they can sort the mail in 8 minutes. How long would it take Kathy to sort the mail alone?

6. One pipe can fill a tank in 4 hours. A second pipe also requires 4 hours but a third needs three hours. How long will it take to fill the tank if all three pipes are open?

Logic Break

Village Occupations

Clark, Jones, Morgan and Smith are four people whose occupations are salesperson, pharmacist, grocer and police officer, though not necessarily in that order. Use the following statements to determine each person's occupation.

1. Clark and Jones are neighbors and take turns driving each other to work.

2. The grocer makes more money than Morgan.

3. Clark beats Smith regularly at bowling.

4. The salesperson always walks to work.

5. The police officer does not live near Clark.

6. The only time Morgan and the police officer ever met was when Morgan was stopped for speeding.

7. The grocer doesn't bowl.

	Salesperson	Pharmacist	Grocer	Police Officer
Clark				
Jones				
Morgan				
Smith				

Birthdays

Make your own matrix.

One week there is a birthday party every day. No two children are invited to the same party. Find out the day that each child attends a party. Start your matrix with Sunday and continue through Saturday.

1. Lisa and Pat don't go to a party on a Friday or a Saturday.

2. Pat and Alice don't go on a Tuesday, but Sandy does.

3. Jennifer goes to a party on Wednesday.

4. Jim goes to a party the day after Jennifer.

5. Lisa goes to a party the day before Pat.

6. Paul goes to a party on a Saturday.

Logic Break

Hobbies

Make your own matrix.

Maureen, Joan, Robert and Bryan each have two favorite hobbies, which include collections. The collections are seashells, stamps, baseball cards, coins, comic books, dolls, bugs and rocks. No two children collect the same things. Find out the two collections each child has.

1. Maureen always finds things for both her collections outdoors.

2. Joan's friend enjoys collecting stamps.

3. One of Bryan's friends enjoys collecting coins.

4. The person who collects comics does not collect baseball cards.

5. One of Bryan's hobbies involves lots of reading.

6. Joan's family has a beach house; this is very helpful for one of her collections.

7. One of the girls collects dolls.

Neighbors

Make your own matrix.

Billy Brown, Willy White, Bobby Blue and George Green all live on the same street. Their houses are painted brown, white, blue and green, but no boy lives in a house that matches his last name. Also, each boy has a pet, and its name does not begin with the same letter as its owner's name. Also, you must find out the location of each house—is it the first, second, third or fourth on the block?

1. George Green owns the bear.

2. Willy White owns the bull.

3. The white house is the last one on the street.

4. Neither the bear nor the bull live next to the first house.

5. Bobby Blue's house is not green.

6. The boy who owns the whale lives in the green house.

7. The gorilla lives in the first house, which is brown.

Linear Equations and Inequalities

 Keep in mind...
Minds are like parachutes—they only function when open.

Graphing with Ordered Pairs

I. Find the coordinates of the indicated point.

1. A

2. I

3. H

4. C

5. E

6. N

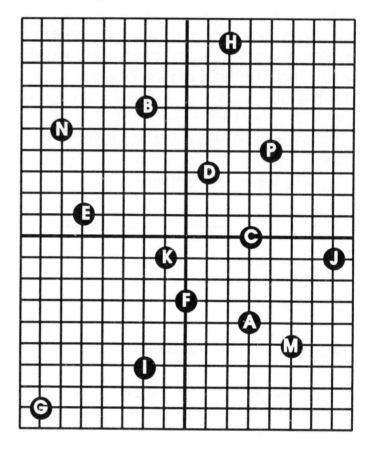

II. Name the graph (letter) of each ordered pair.

7. (-2, 6)

8. (0, -3)

9. (5, -5)

10. (-1, -1)

11. (-7, -8)

12. (7, -1)

13. The coordinates are equal.

14. The y-coordinate is three times the x-coordinate.

III. Name the quadrant or axis on which each point lies.

15. (-4, 3)

16. (0, 6)

17. (4, -2)

18. (-1, -1)

19. (-2, 0)

20. (1, 2)

Graphing Equations

Graph each equation by plotting points. Use your own graph paper.

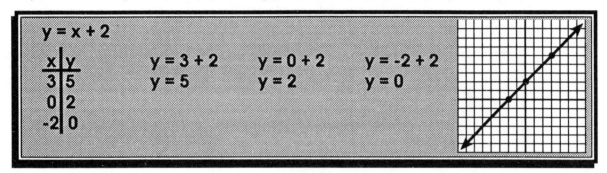

$y = x + 2$

x	y
3	5
0	2
-2	0

$y = 3 + 2$ $y = 0 + 2$ $y = -2 + 2$
$y = 5$ $y = 2$ $y = 0$

1. $y = x + 3$

5. $x = -7$

2. $y = -2x + 4$

6. $y = -3x + 5$

x	y
2	
0	
-1	

3. $x + y = 2$

7. $y = 5 - x$

x	y
7	
3	
0	

4. $3x + y = 9$

8. $3x + 4y = 12$

x	y
4	
0	
-4	

Finding the Slope of a Line

I. Slope = $\dfrac{\text{vertical change}}{\text{horizontal change}}$

Identify the slope of the line using the graph.

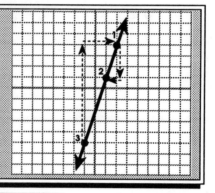

Using points 1 & 2
vertical change = -3
horizontal change = -1

slope = $\dfrac{-3}{-1}$ = 3

1.

2.

3.

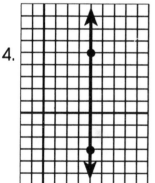

4.

5.

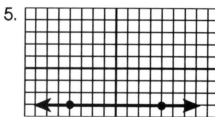

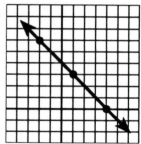

II. Slope = $\dfrac{\text{change in y-values}}{\text{change in x-values}} = \dfrac{y_2 - y_1}{x_2 - x_1}$

Find the slope of the line passing through the given points.

(-1, 5) (3, -2)

slope = $\dfrac{-2 - 5}{3 - (-1)} = \dfrac{-7}{4}$

6. (0, 0) (3, 5)

7. (5, -2) (-7, 4)

8. (-6, 3) (-2, -9)

9. (6, -9) (-4, 3)

10. (-3, -11) (2, -7)

11. (7, 3) (-8, 3)

12. (0, 0) (4, -3)

13. (-2, -3) (2, 5)

14. (-4, 8) (-4, -3)

Slope-Intercept Form

$$4x + y = 3$$
$$4x - 4x + y = -4x + 3$$
$$y = -4x + 3$$

I. Solve for y.

1. $x + y = 3$
2. $2x - y = 7$
3. $-6 + 2y = 10x$
4. $3y - 6x + 12 = 0$

$$9x - 3y = -6$$
$$y = 3x + 2$$
$$m = \frac{3}{1}$$
$$y_0 = 2$$

II. Solve for y, state the m and y_0.

5. $2y - 6x = 2$
6. $y - 4x = -3$
7. $4y = 5x + 12$
8. $2x - 3y = 5$

III. Graph the line by 1.) solving for y 2.) using m and y_0.

9. $4x + y = -8$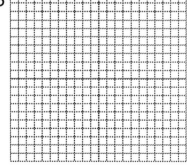

10. $y - 3x = -9$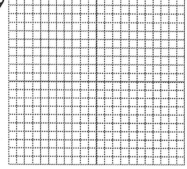

11. $2x - 4y = -16$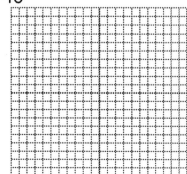

12. $3x + 3y + 4 = 0$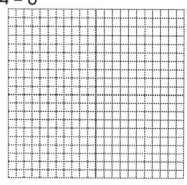

...More Slope-Intercept Form

Graph from the slope-intercept form: $y = mx + b$.

m = slope
b = y-intercept

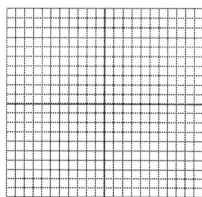

y = 4x + 2
1) Plot y-intercept
   b = 2 $\Rightarrow$ (0, 2)
2) Find other points using slope
   m = 4 $\Rightarrow$ $\frac{4}{1}$ or $\frac{-4}{-1}$
3) Connect points.

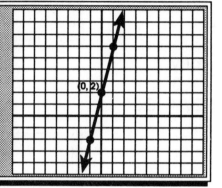

1. $y = 2x - 4$

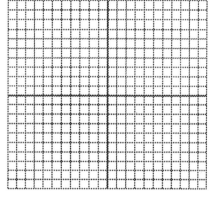

2. $3x - y = 7$

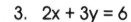

3. $2x + 3y = 6$

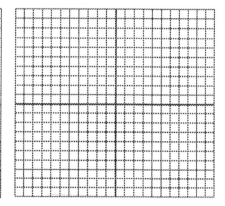

4. $y = -\frac{3}{2}x + 1$

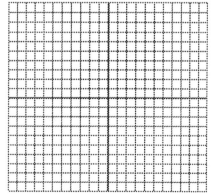

5. $x - 4y + 8 = 0$

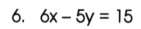

6. $6x - 5y = 15$

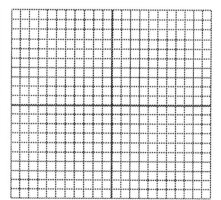

X and Y Intercepts

I. Find the x and y intercepts.

$$2x + y = 3$$
To find x intercept, let $y = 0$. To find y-intercept, let $x = 0$.
$$2x + 0 = 3 \qquad\qquad\qquad 2 \cdot 0 + y = 3$$
$$2x = 3 \qquad\qquad\qquad\qquad y = 3 \; (0, 3)$$
$$x = \frac{3}{2} \quad (\frac{3}{2}, 0)$$

1. $3x + 4y = 12$

2. $4x + y = 2$

3. $5x - 4y = 15$

4. $2x - 2y = -4$

5. $3x + y = -9$

6. $4x - 2y - 8 = 0$

II. Find the x and y intercepts. Then graph.

7. $x + 2y = 5$

8. $2x - 5y = 0$

9. $4x - 3y = -2$

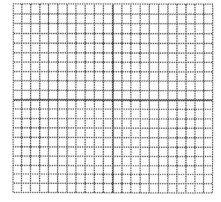
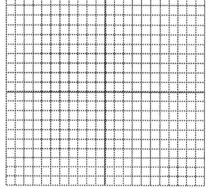
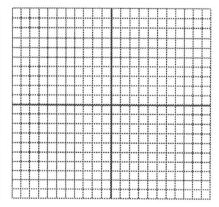

10. $3x + 2y = 6$

11. $5x - 7y = 12$

12. $8x + 10y = 50$

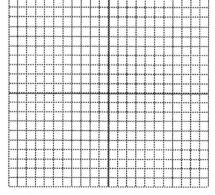
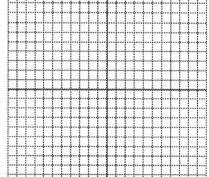
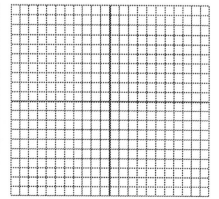

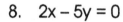
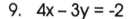

Writing an Equation of a Line in Standard Form: $Ax + By = C$

I. Put in standard form.

$$y = -\frac{2}{5}x + 3$$
$$-5y = 2x - 15$$
$$-2x - 5y = -15$$
$$2x + 5y = 15$$

1. $y = -\frac{3}{4}x + 2$

2. $y = \frac{1}{2}x - 2$

3. $y = 3x + 6$

4. $y = -x - 5$

5. $y = \frac{3}{4}x + \frac{1}{2}$

6. $y = -\frac{1}{4}x + 8$

II. Find the equation of a line in standard form using the slope-intercept form.

$$m = -\frac{3}{4} \qquad\qquad y_0 = 2$$
$$y = -\frac{3}{4}x + 2$$
$$\frac{3}{4}x + y = 2$$
$$3x + 4y = 8$$

7. $m = 3 \qquad y_0 = -\frac{1}{2}$

8. $m = \frac{5}{4} \qquad y_0 = 2$

9. $m = -\frac{2}{3} \qquad y_0 = \frac{3}{5}$

10. $m = 4 \qquad y_0 = -3$

11. $m = \frac{3}{4} \qquad y_0 = \frac{1}{2}$

12. $m = \frac{7}{2} \qquad y_0 = -\frac{3}{4}$

13. $m = 0 \qquad y_0 = -3$

...More Writing an Equation of a Line in Standard Form: $Ax + By = C$

III. Find the equation of the line in standard form using the point-slope formula.

> $m = 3 \ (1, 2)$
>
> $3 = \dfrac{y - 2}{x - 1}$
>
> $3(x - 1) = y - 2$
> $3x - 3 = y - 2$
> $3x = y + 1$
> $3x - y = 1$
>
> Let (x, y) be any other point on the line.
> Use slope formula:
>
> $m = \dfrac{y_2 - y_1}{x_2 - x_1}$
>
> or point-slope formula:
> $y_2 - y_1 = m(x_2 - x_1)$

1. $m = -3, (4, 5)$

2. $m = -2, (1, 3)$

3. $m = 0, (4, -6)$

4. $m = \dfrac{3}{4}, (1, 0)$

5. no slope, $(-3, \dfrac{3}{4})$

6. $m = -1, (-1, 4)$

7. $m = -\dfrac{1}{2}, (6, -3)$

8. $m = 1, (1, -4)$

9. $m = \dfrac{1}{4}, (-4, 3)$

10. $m = \dfrac{1}{3}, (-3, -2)$

11. $m = \dfrac{2}{3}, (-1, 1)$

12. $m = 0, (7, -4)$

13. $m = -\dfrac{2}{1}, (-2, -7)$

14. $m = \dfrac{5}{1}, (-2, 0)$

...More Writing an Equation of a Line in Standard Form: Ax + By = C

IV. Find the equation of the line in standard form using 1) slope and then
2) point-slope formula.

$$(-3, 4) \ (4, 7)$$

$$m = \frac{7-4}{4-(-3)} = \frac{3}{7}$$

$$\frac{3}{7} = \frac{y-7}{x-4}$$

$$y - -4 = \frac{3}{7}(x+3)$$

$$7y - 28 = 3x + 9$$

$$3x - 7y = -37$$

1. (2, 1)   (4, 0)

2. (5, 2)   (2, -1)

3. (4, -3)   (0, 3)

4. (-2, -3)   (-1, 2)

5. (0, 0)   (-1, -2)

6. (6, -3)   (-2, -3)

7. (2, 3)   (-1, 5)

8. (4, 8)   (4, -2)

9. (5, 8)   (3, 2)

10. (-2, 5)   (3, -10)

11. (0, 2)   (-4, 2)

12. (-1, -1)   (0, -4)

13. (-3, 6)   (-3, 2)

14. (-6, 6)   (3, 3)

Graphing Linear Inequalities

$y < -\frac{1}{2}x + 1$

1.) Graph $y = -\frac{1}{2}x + 1$ as a dotted line.

2.) Choose a point in one half-plane and substitute. Try (0, 3):

$3 < -\frac{1}{2} \cdot 0 + 1 = 3 < 1 =$ False

3.) Shade half-plane that does not contain (0, 3).

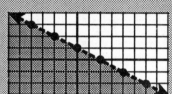

$3x - 4y \leq 12 \Longrightarrow y \geq \frac{3}{4}x - 3$

1.) Graph $y \geq \frac{3}{4}x - 3$ as a solid line.

2.) Choose a point in one half-plane and substitute. Try (0, 0):

$0 \geq \frac{3}{4} \cdot -3 \Longrightarrow 0 \geq -3 \Longrightarrow$ True

3.) Shade the half-plane that contains (0, 0).

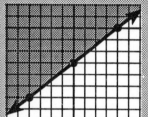

1. $y > x + 1$

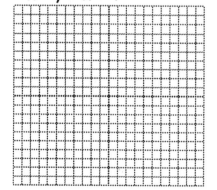

2. $3x - y \leq 6$

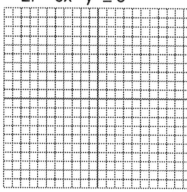

3. $y + 5 \leq 0$

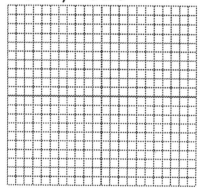

4. $y \geq 2x - 3$

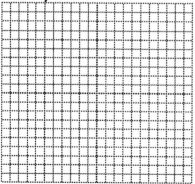

5. $x + y < 3$

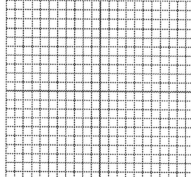

6. $2x + y > -8$

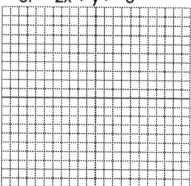

Systems of Equations: Graphic Method

Solve by graphing.

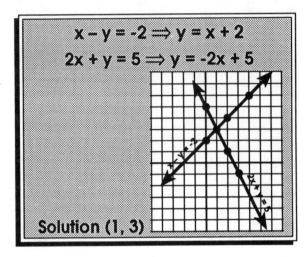

$$x - y = -2 \implies y = x + 2$$
$$2x + y = 5 \implies y = -2x + 5$$

Solution (1, 3)

1. x – y = 6
    2x + y = 0

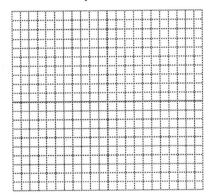

2. 2x –2y = -4
    y = 2

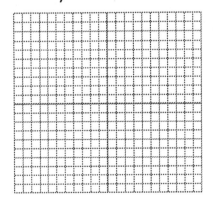

3. 2x – y = 1
    3x + y = -6

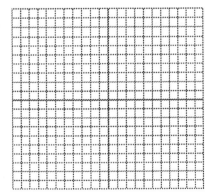

4. x + 2y = 4
    2x – y = 8

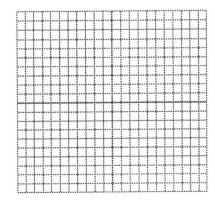

5. 2x – y = 5
    x – y = 1

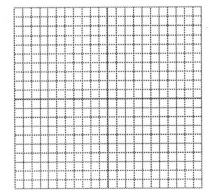

6. x = 3
    y = -2

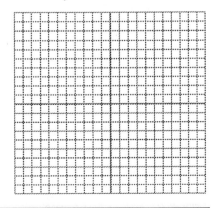

Systems of Equations: Elimination Method

$$x + y = 6$$
$$x - y = 4$$

$$x + y = 6$$
$$\underline{+ x - y = 4}$$
$$2x \quad = 10$$
$$x = 5$$

$$x + y = 6 \Rightarrow 5 + y = 6$$
$$y = 1$$

Solution (5, 1)

$$3y = -7x + 7 \Rightarrow 7x + 3y = 7$$
$$2y = 7x - 7 \Rightarrow \underline{- (7x - 2y = 7)}$$
$$5y = 0$$
$$y = 0$$

$$2y = 7x - 7 \Rightarrow 0 = 7x - 7$$
$$7 = 7x$$
$$1 = X$$

Solution (1, 0)

1. $2x + y = -6$
    $3x + y = -10$

2. $8x - y = 20$
    $-5x + y = -8$

3. $2x + y = 0$
    $2x - 3y = -8$

4. $5x + 3y = 10$
    $2x - 3y = 4$

5. $9x - 3y = 9$
    $x + 3y = 11$

6. $x + 3y = 9$
    $x - 2y = -6$

7. $2x + y = 4$
    $2x + 2y = 2$

8. $7y + 15 = 3x$
    $15 = 3x + 2y$

9. $25x = 91 - 16y$
    $16y = 64 - 16x$

10. $4x - 2y = -2$
    $4x + 3y = -12$

11. $2x + y = -7$
    $y = 3x + 3$

12. $3x = -2y + 10$
    $x = 2y + 6$

13. $x + 4y = 2$
    $x - 2y = 8$

14. $x + 5y + 11 = 0$
    $3x - 5y - 7 = 0$

Linear Equations and Inequalities

Systems of Equations: More Elimination Method

$$2x + 5y = 11 \qquad 4x + 10y = 22$$
$$3x - 2y = -12 \qquad \underline{+\ 15x - 10y = -60}$$
$$19x \qquad = -38$$
$$\text{Solution } (-2, 3) \qquad x = -2$$

1. $3x - y = 3$
   $x + 3y = 11$

2. $4x + 2y = 14$
   $3x - y = 8$

3. $4x - y = 9$
   $3x - 5y = 11$

4. $2x + 2y = -16$
   $4x - 4y = 32$

5. $3x - 5y = 11$
   $4x + 3y = 5$

6. $2x - 7y = 8$
   $3x - 4y = -1$

7. $5x - 2y = 4$
   $3x - 4y = -6$

8. $6x + 5y = -2$
   $2x + 3y = 6$

9. $2x + 3y = 4$
   $5x + 4y = 3$

10. $5x - 2y = 17$
    $2x + 3y = 3$

11. $x - 2y = -8$
    $3x + y = 4$

12. $3x + 5y = 9$
    $9x + 2y = -12$

13. $2x + 3y = 14$
    $-2y + 3x = -5$

14. $5x + 2y = -8$
    $2x - 5y = -9$

Systems of Equations: Substitution Method

$$x - 5y = 10 \qquad\qquad x - 5(2x + 7) = 10$$
$$-2x + y = 7 \Longrightarrow y = 2x + 7 \qquad x - 10x - 35 = 10$$
$$\text{Solution } (-5, -3) \qquad\qquad -9x - 35 = 10$$
$$-9x = 45$$
$$x = -5$$

1. $y = 5 - 4x$
   $3x - 2y = 12$

2. $3x + 2y = 8$
   $x = 3y + 10$

3. $3x - 4y = -15$
   $5x + y = -2$

4. $x + y = 2$
   $3x + 2y = 5$

5. $x = 3 - 3y$
   $4y = x + 11$

6. $x - y = -15$
   $x + y = -5$

7. $2x + y = -6$
   $3x + y = -10$

8. $y = -x + 6$
   $x - 2y = -6$

9. $2y - x = 6$
   $3y - x = 4$

10. $5x - 6y = 16$
    $5x + y = 2$

11. $y = 3x$
    $x + y = 8$

12. $x - 3y = -5$
    $2x + y = 11$

13. $-x + y = 5$
    $y = -3x + 1$

14. $2x = 3y$
    $x = 3y - 3$

Solving Problems with Two Variables

Set up and solve each equation.

> If 8 pens and 7 pencils cost $3.37 while 5 pens and 11 pencils cost
> $3.10, how much does each pen and each pencil cost?
>
> Let x = cost of 1 pen   Let y = cost of 1 pencil $8x + 7 \cdot 15 = 337$
> $8x + 7y = 337$ $-40x - 35y = -1685$ $8x + 105 = 337$
> $5x + 11y = 310$ $\underline{40x + 88y = 2480}$ $8x = 232$
> $53y = 795$ $x = 29$
> $y = 15$
>
> Pens cost $.29 and pencils cost $.15.

1. A rectangle has a perimeter of 18 cm. Its length is 5 cm greater than its width. Find the dimensions.

2. Timmy has 180 marbles, some plain and some colored. If there are 32 more plain marbles than colored marbles, how many colored marbles does he have?

3. A theater sold 900 tickets to a play. Floor seats cost $12 each and balcony seats $10 each. Total receipts were $9780. How many of each type of ticket were sold?

4. Ryan and Karl spent 28 hours building a tree house. Ryan worked 4 more hours than Karl. How many hours did each work?

5. The difference between seven times one number and three times a second number is 25. The sum of twice the first and five times the second is 95. Find the numbers.

6. The sum of two numbers is 36. Their difference is 6. Find the numbers.

7. The volleyball club has 41 members. There are 3 more boys than girls. How many girls are there?

8. The sum of two numbers is 15. Twice one number equals 3 times the other. Find the numbers.

Graphing Systems of Linear Inequalities

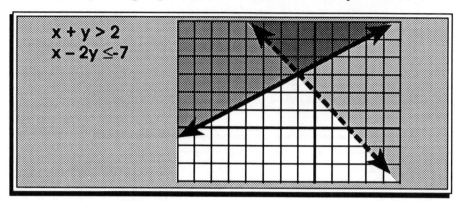

$x + y > 2$
$x - 2y \leq -7$

1. $y \geq x - 1$
    $y \leq -2x + 1$

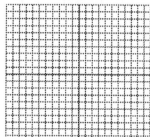

5. $x + y \geq 0$
    $x - y > 0$

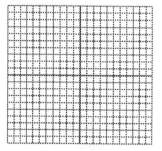

2. $2x - y > 3$
    $x + y > 3$

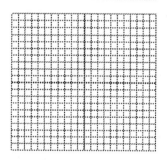

6. $y > \dfrac{1}{2}x + 3$
    $y > 3$

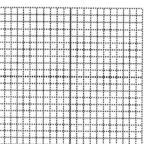

3. $y \geq x$
    $y \geq -x$

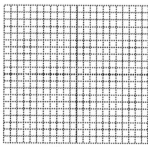

7. $3y - x \geq 3$
    $x \leq -2$

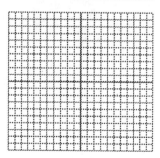

4. $y \leq x + 2$
    $y > 2 - x$

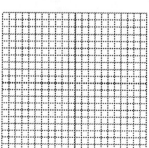

8. $y < 3$
    $x - y < 0$

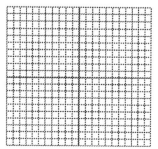

Just for Fun

Try and de-code these words and phrases.

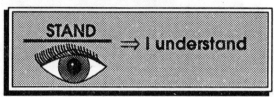

1. sand	**2.** MOMANON	**3.** R|E|A|D	**4.** WEAR LONG
5. MCE MCE MCE	**6.** HANDS / ACTIVITIES	**7.** KEND VACATION	**8.** FALUTING
9. .SIGN. ••••••••	**10.** LET GONES GONES B GONES GONES	**11.** Thought Clever	**12.** luck luck luck luck luck luck luck luck luck
13. MAN BOARD	**14.** ROSES	**15.** (moon) π π ★ π	**16.** T O U C H

Keep in mind...
You can forget your own problems if you can help someone solve theirs.

Simplifying Radicals

All variables are non-negative numbers.

$$\sqrt{18x^3y^2} = \sqrt{9 \cdot 2 \cdot x^2 \cdot x \cdot y^2}$$
$$= 3xy\sqrt{2x}$$

1. $\sqrt{100}$

2. $\sqrt{75}$

3. $-\sqrt{144a^2}$

4. $\sqrt{128x^3}$

5. $2\sqrt{1000}$

6. $\sqrt{15a^8b}$

7. $\sqrt{16c^2d^2}$

8. $2\sqrt{27x^5y}$

9. $-\sqrt{20xy^2}$

10. $\sqrt{50a^3}$

11. $\sqrt{96bc^2d^5}$

12. $-3\sqrt{150a^7c^2}$

13. $\sqrt{27a^2}$

14. $2\sqrt{50x^2yz^3}$

15. $\sqrt{243m^5n^2}$

16. $-\sqrt{320y^9z^{10}}$

Products of Radicals

All variables are non-negative numbers.

Products — Multiply radicals and simplify.

$$4\sqrt{3} \cdot 2\sqrt{18} = 8\sqrt{54} = 8\sqrt{9 \cdot 6} = 8 \cdot 3\sqrt{6} = 24\sqrt{6}$$
$$\sqrt{2a} \cdot \sqrt{6a} = \sqrt{12a^2} = \sqrt{4 \cdot 3 \cdot a^2} = 2a\sqrt{3}$$

1. $\sqrt{2} \cdot \sqrt{8}$

2. $5\sqrt{5} \cdot 3\sqrt{14}$

3. $\sqrt{5b} \cdot \sqrt{10b}$

4. $a\sqrt{2x} \cdot x\sqrt{6x}$

5. $2m\sqrt{7mn} \cdot 3\sqrt{7m}$

6. $-5a\sqrt{2a^4b} \cdot 4b\sqrt{12a^3b^4}$

7. $2\sqrt{5}(-\sqrt{3x})$

8. $5\sqrt{6} \cdot 2\sqrt{2}$

9. $\sqrt{x} \cdot \sqrt{9x}$

10. $\sqrt{2x} \cdot \sqrt{10x^2y}$

11. $4x\sqrt{5} \cdot \sqrt{8xy^2}$

12. $2\sqrt{x^3} \cdot 4\sqrt{x}$

13. $-7\sqrt{3y} \cdot \sqrt{6y}$

14. $\sqrt{xy} \cdot \sqrt{xy}$

92

Quotients of Radicals

Quotients—Rationalizing the denominator.

$$\sqrt{\frac{7}{8}} = \frac{\sqrt{7}}{\sqrt{8}} = \frac{\sqrt{2}}{\sqrt{2}} = \frac{\sqrt{14}}{\sqrt{16}} = \frac{\sqrt{14}}{4}$$

$$\sqrt{\frac{2a^4b^3}{27x^3}} = \frac{\sqrt{2a^4b^3}}{\sqrt{27x^3}} \cdot \frac{\sqrt{3x}}{\sqrt{3x}} = \frac{\sqrt{6a^4b^3x}}{\sqrt{81x^4}} = \frac{a^2b\sqrt{6bx}}{9x^2}$$

1. $\sqrt{\dfrac{2ab^2}{c^2d}}$

2. $\sqrt{\dfrac{2x}{3y}}$

3. $\sqrt{\dfrac{19x^2}{32}}$

4. $\sqrt{\dfrac{4a^2b}{x^8y^7}}$

5. $x\sqrt{\dfrac{5d}{3x^2}}$

6. $\sqrt{\dfrac{7a^2}{8cd}}$

7. $\sqrt{\dfrac{n^2}{7}}$

8. $\sqrt{\dfrac{8}{25}}$

9. $\dfrac{3\sqrt{2}}{\sqrt{3}}$

10. $\sqrt{\dfrac{4x^2}{25}}$

11. $\sqrt{\dfrac{11y^3}{9}}$

12. $\sqrt{\dfrac{25}{3x}}$

13. $\sqrt{\dfrac{3}{6x^3}}$

14. $\dfrac{\sqrt{8x^2y}}{\sqrt{2y}}$

Radicals

Sums and Differences of Radicals

$$3\sqrt{9xy^4} - y\sqrt{16xy^2} + 2y^2\sqrt{25x} = 9y^2\sqrt{x} - 4y^2\sqrt{x} + 10y^2\sqrt{x} = 15y^2\sqrt{x}$$

$$10\sqrt{\frac{1}{5}} + 4\sqrt{18} + 3\sqrt{45} - 8\sqrt{\frac{1}{2}} = 2\sqrt{5} + 12\sqrt{2} + 9\sqrt{5} - 4\sqrt{2} = 11\sqrt{5} + 8\sqrt{2}$$

1. $3\sqrt{7} - 4\sqrt{7} + 2\sqrt{7}$

2. $4\sqrt{27} - 2\sqrt{48} + \sqrt{147}$

3. $5\sqrt{3} - 4\sqrt{7} - 3\sqrt{3} + \sqrt{7}$

4. $5\sqrt{x} - 3\sqrt{x} + a\sqrt{x}$

5. $4\sqrt{\frac{1}{2}} + 2\sqrt{18} - 6\sqrt{\frac{2}{9}}$

6. $\sqrt{63} - \sqrt{28} - \sqrt{7}$

7. $6\sqrt{3} - 2\sqrt{75} + 4\sqrt{\frac{3}{16}}$

8. $\sqrt{50} + \sqrt{98} - \sqrt{75} + \sqrt{27}$

9. $2x\sqrt{ab} - 2y\sqrt{ab} + 4x\sqrt{ab}$

10. $2b\sqrt{3c} + b\sqrt{5c} + b\sqrt{3c} - 2b\sqrt{5c}$

11. $4\sqrt{c^3d^3} + 3cd\sqrt{4cd} - 2c\sqrt{9cd^3}$

12. $8\sqrt{12} - 10\sqrt{\frac{1}{5}} - 108 + \sqrt{125}$

13. $x\sqrt{4x} + \sqrt{x^3}$

14. $3x\sqrt{7} + \sqrt{28x^2} - \sqrt{63x^2}$

Combined Operations with Radicals

1. $\sqrt{\dfrac{8}{9}} + 2\sqrt{\dfrac{1}{2}} - 3\sqrt{\dfrac{9}{8}}$

8. $\sqrt{100x} - \sqrt{9x}$

2. $3\sqrt{2x^3} - \sqrt{8x^3}$

9. $\sqrt{12y^3} - 2\sqrt{3y^3} + \sqrt{27y^3}$

3. $\sqrt{3}(\sqrt{3} + 2)$

10. $\sqrt{25 - \dfrac{25}{4}}$

4. $\sqrt{7}(8 + \sqrt{12})$

11. $\sqrt{\dfrac{60m^3n}{5m}}$

5. $\sqrt{5}(\sqrt{2} - \sqrt{3})$

12. $2x\sqrt{25x} + x\sqrt{4x} - 3x\sqrt{9x}$

6. $(\sqrt{5} - 2)(\sqrt{5} + 2)$

13. $\dfrac{2}{\sqrt{6} - 3}$

7. $(8 + \sqrt{3})(8 - \sqrt{3})$

14. $\dfrac{4}{-2 + \sqrt{7}}$

Solving Radical Equations

$3 + \sqrt{x} = 6$	$\sqrt{x} = 3$	$(\sqrt{x})^2 = (3)^2$	$x = 9$

1. $\sqrt{x-1} = 4$

2. $4 = 5\sqrt{x}$

3. $\sqrt{x+3} = 1$

4. $8 = \sqrt{5a+1}$

5. $2\sqrt{x} = 5$

6. $\sqrt{7+3x} = 4$

7. $\sqrt{4-x} = 7$

8. $4 + \sqrt{x+1} = 5$

9. $\dfrac{\sqrt{5-2x}}{3} = 1$

10. $\sqrt{4x-3} = \sqrt{x}$

11. $5 = \dfrac{15}{\sqrt{2a-3}}$

12. $6 - \sqrt{y-5} = 3$

13. $2\sqrt{5} = 3\sqrt{x}$

14. $2\sqrt{x} = 4\sqrt{3}$

Solving Quadratic Equations

$$(x - 5)^2 = 36$$
$$\sqrt{(x - 5)^2} = \sqrt{36}$$
$$x - 5 = \pm 6$$
$$x = 11, -1$$

1. $x^2 = 25$

2. $(x - 2)^2 = 9$

3. $2y^2 = 32$

4. $x^2 - 49 = 0$

5. $3a^2 - 1 = 11$

6. $(2x - 5)^2 = 49$

7. $(x + 1)^2 = 4$

8. $(x + 17)^2 = 49$

9. $(x + 3)^2 = 0$

10. $4(y + 5)^2 = 4$

11. $(2x - 6)^2 = 16$

12. $3(2y + 7)^2 = 27$

The Quadratic Formula

$$x = \frac{-b \pm \sqrt{b^2 - 4ac}}{2a}$$

$$3x^2 - 5x - 4 = 0$$

$$a = 3, \quad b = -5, \quad c = -4 \implies \frac{5 \pm \sqrt{25 - 4\,(3)\,(-4)}}{6} = \frac{5 \pm \sqrt{73}}{6}$$

Solve using the quadratic formula.

1. $x^2 - 2x - 8 = 0$

2. $y^2 + 11y + 10 = 0$

3. $x^2 + 2x - 4 = 0$

4. $y^2 + 5y - 7 = 0$

5. $2x^2 - 3x - 5 = 0$

6. $2y^2 + 4y = 1$

7. $7x^2 + 4x - 5 = 0$

8. $3x^2 + 10x + 5 = 0$

9. $2y^2 = 3y + 4$

10. $8x^2 + 7x - 2 = 0$

11. $x^2 = 4x$

12. $\dfrac{3}{x-1} - 4 = \dfrac{1}{x+1}$

Completing the Square

$$x^2 + 2x - 5 = 0$$
$$x^2 + 2x + 1 = 5 + 1$$
$$(x + 1)^2 = 6$$
$$x + 1 = \pm \sqrt{6}$$
$$x = -1 \pm \sqrt{6}$$

Solve by completing the square.

1. $y^2 + 10y - 11 = 0$

2. $x^2 + 4x - 12 = 0$

3. $y^2 + 6y = -8$

4. $x^2 - 14x + 40 = 0$

5. $x^2 - 16x = -60$

6. $4x^2 - 17x + 4 = 0$

7. $2a^2 - 2a - 1 = 0$

8. $x^2 = -5x + 3$

9. $y^2 - 7y - 9 = 0$

10. $2x = 5 + \dfrac{4}{x}$

Problem Solving with Quadratic Equations

1. Two consecutive, positive, odd numbers have a product of 675. What are the numbers?

2. The sum of the squares of two consecutive, positive, odd numbers is 74. What is the number?

3. The perimeter of a rectangular pool is 32 meters, and its area is 48 square meters. What are its dimensions?

4. The sum of the squares of two consecutive, positive numbers is 85. Find the numbers.

5. A rectangular piece of artwork is 4 meters wide and 6 meters long. It is surrounded by a uniform sidewalk. If the area of the sidewalk is 39 square meters, how wide is the sidewalk?

6. There are two positive numbers such that one is 6 less than twice the other. The difference of the squares of the two numbers is 1311. Find the numbers.

Pythagorean Theorem: $a^2 + b^2 = c^2$

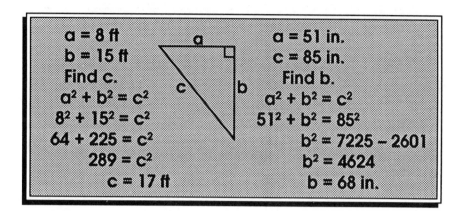

a = 8 ft
b = 15 ft
Find c.
$a^2 + b^2 = c^2$
$8^2 + 15^2 = c^2$
$64 + 225 = c^2$
$289 = c^2$
$c = 17$ ft

a = 51 in.
c = 85 in.
Find b.
$a^2 + b^2 = c^2$
$51^2 + b^2 = 85^2$
$b^2 = 7225 - 2601$
$b^2 = 4624$
$b = 68$ in.

Find the missing side of the right triangle.

1. a = 6 ft   b = 8 ft

2. a = 24 m   b = 7m

3. a = 16 m   b = 30m

4. a = 5 in.   b = 5 in.

5. a = 65 cm   c = 97 cm

6. a = 15 mm   c = 17 mm

7. b = 17 ft   c = 19 ft

8. a = 5 cm   b = 12 cm

9. b = 20 in.   c = 101 in.

10. a = 28 in.   c = 197 in.

11. b = 32 cm   c = 40 cm

12. a = 8.2 m   c = 9.5 m

Problem Solving and the Pythagorean Theorem

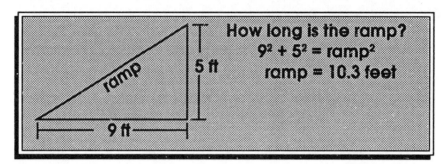

How long is the ramp?
$9^2 + 5^2 = ramp^2$
ramp = 10.3 feet

1. How high is the flagpole?

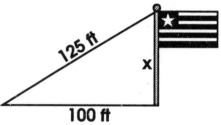

2. How long is the longest side of the sail?

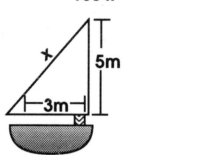

3. A 10-foot ladder is leaning against a house with its base 4 feet from the base of the house. How far up the house does the ladder touch the house?
   (Hint: draw a picture.)

4. A 5-foot tall tree casts an 8-foot shadow on the ground. How far is it from the end of the shadow to the top of the tree?
   (Hint: draw a picture.)

5. A guy wire is secured into the ground 15 feet from the base of a 36-foot pole. How long is the guy wire if it is attached at the top of the 36-foot pole?
   (Hint: draw a picture.)

6. An airplane travels due east 65 miles, then due north 72 miles. How far is the airplane from its starting point?
   (Hint: draw a picture.)

Answer Key

Operations with Real Numbers

Adding Real Numbers

$$-7 + 3 = -4$$

1. $9 + (-6)$ **3**
2. $-54 + -6 + -3 + 42$ **-21**
3. $-35 + 1 + -3 + 6$ **-31**
4. $4 + -15 + -13 + 19$ **-5**
5. $32 + -15 + 17$ **34**
6. $-5 + 17 + (-6) + 4$ **10**
7. $7 + 0 + -7$ **0**
8. $11 + -5 + 17 + -5 + 3$ **21**
9. $1.4 + (-7.2)$ **-5.8**
10. $-1.6 + (-2.5)$ **-4.1**
11. $2.9 + -3.8$ **-.9**
12. $6.25 + -3.45 + .50$ **3.3**
13. $-9\frac{1}{3} + 4\frac{3}{4}$ **$-4\frac{7}{12}$**
14. $-3\frac{2}{3} + (-2\frac{1}{6}) + 3$ **$-2\frac{5}{6}$**
15. $-2\frac{1}{3} + 5\frac{3}{4}$ **$3\frac{5}{12}$**
16. $7\frac{1}{3} + (-2\frac{5}{6})$ **$4\frac{1}{2}$**

17. Susie had $500 in her savings account on Tuesday. She withdrew $200 on Wednesday, then deposited $350 on Thursday. What is the new balance in the account? **$650**

18. The temperature at 8:00 a.m. was -10° F. It rose 15° by noon. What was the temperature at noon? **5°F**

Page 1

Operations with Real Numbers

Subtracting Real Numbers

$$7 - (-3) = 7 + 3 = 10$$

1. $32 - 212$ **-180**
2. $19 - (-12)$ **31**
3. $-201 - (-42)$ **-159**
4. $22 - 33 - (-11)$ **0**
5. $7 - (-5) - 6 - 7$ **-1**
6. $33 - 14 - 42 + 16 - 26$ **-33**
7. $0 - 14$ **-14**
8. $7 - (-16)$ **23**
9. $-17 - 8$ **-25**
10. $-9 - (-6)$ **-3**
11. $2.9 - 3.8$ **-.9**
12. $8 - 3.2$ **4.8**
13. $12.3 - 6.7 - 3.5 + 1.8$ **3.9**
14. $-\frac{2}{3} - \frac{1}{12} - (-\frac{1}{4})$ **$-\frac{1}{2}$**
15. $-\frac{3}{4} - \frac{1}{2}$ **$-1\frac{1}{4}$**
16. $-\frac{2}{3} - (-\frac{5}{6})$ **$\frac{1}{6}$**

17. The temperature is currently 9° F. At 9:00 a.m. this morning it was -3° F. What was the change in temperature? **12°**

18. The lowest temperature ever recorded in city A was -37° F. The lowest temperature ever recorded in city B was -63° F. Find the difference between the two temperatures. **26°**

Page 2

Operations with Real Numbers

Multiplying Real Numbers

$$(-\frac{1}{2})(-\frac{3}{4}) = \frac{3}{8}$$

1. $-4 \cdot 15$ **-60**
2. $(-6)(-8)$ **48**
3. $(-10)(-3)(4)$ **120**
4. $(-21)(-4)(0)$ **0**
5. $(-3)(-3)(-3)$ **-27**
6. $(-3)(8)$ **-24**
7. $(-5)(0)$ **0**
8. $14(-6)$ **-84**
9. -40×-9 **360**
10. $(6)(-8)(2)$ **-96**
11. $(4)(-2)(-5)$ **40**
12. $(-7)(1.5)$ **-10.5**
13. $(1.2)(-5)$ **-6**
14. $(6.5)(1)(-3)$ **-19.5**
15. $(-6)(-2.7)$ **16.2**
16. $(\frac{2}{3})(-6)$ **-4**
17. $(-2.3)(5)(-2)$ **23**
18. $(\frac{3}{8})(\frac{5}{6})$ **$\frac{5}{16}$**
19. $(-\frac{5}{8})(-\frac{2}{3})$ **$\frac{5}{12}$**
20. $\frac{1}{7}(-\frac{7}{10})$ **$-\frac{1}{10}$**
21. $(-12)(-\frac{1}{3})(\frac{3}{4})$ **3**
22. $(-6\frac{2}{3})(3\frac{3}{4})$ **-25**
23. $(-4)^2$ **16**
24. $(-1)^3$ **-1**

Page 3

Operations with Real Numbers

Dividing Real Numbers

$$-5.4 \div -9 = .6$$

1. $-91 \div 7$ **-13**
2. $36 \div (-9)$ **-4**
3. $-54 \div (-9)$ **6**
4. $75 \div 15$ **5**
5. $0 \div (-7)$ **0**
6. $\frac{56}{-7}$ **-8**
7. $\frac{-72}{-12}$ **6**
8. $\frac{102}{-17}$ **-6**
9. $600 \div 24$ **25**
10. $\frac{144}{-12}$ **-12**
11. $-48 \div 3$ **-16**
12. $-1.5 \div (-.3)$ **5**
13. $2.4 \div (-1.2)$ **-2**
14. $-1.44 \div (.3)$ **-4.8**
15. $\frac{0}{-4.12}$ **0**
16. $\frac{1}{8} \div -\frac{6}{5}$ **$-5/48$**
17. $-\frac{3}{7} \div -\frac{8}{21}$ **$1\frac{1}{8}$**
18. $-10 \div \frac{1}{3}$ **-30**
19. $-\frac{3}{4} \div (-12)$ **$\frac{1}{16}$**
20. $-15 \div \frac{3}{5}$ **-25**
21. $\frac{4}{5} \div (-\frac{3}{10})$ **$-2\frac{2}{3}$**
22. $-\frac{3}{8} \div (-\frac{3}{4})$ **$\frac{1}{2}$**
23. $\frac{5}{6} \div \frac{4}{9}$ **$1\frac{7}{8}$**
24. $-6\frac{2}{3} \div 3\frac{3}{4}$ **$-1\frac{7}{9}$**

Page 4

Answer Key

Operations with Real Numbers 84
Order of Operations

$2 + (2^2 + 6) \div -2 - 1 = 2 + (4 + 6) \div -2 - 1 = 2 + 10 \div -2 - 1 = 2 + -5 - 1 = -4$

1. $(12 - 8) + 3$ **7**
2. $2 \cdot 6 + 4 \cdot 5$ **32**
3. $25 \div 5 \cdot 4 - 15 \cdot 8$ **-100**
4. $3 + 15 \div 3 - 4$ **4**
5. $15 \div (7 - 2) + 3$ **6**
6. $2(7 + 3) \div 4$ **5**
7. $7 - (8 \cdot 2) \cdot 0$ **7**
8. $2(4 + (6 + 2))$ **14**
9. $20 \div (2 + (7 - 4))$ **4**
10. $6(-9 + 4) + 3 - 1$ **-11**
11. $6 - 4(6 + 2)$ **-26**
12. $12 \div ((8 + 2) \cdot (3 + 3))$ **3**
13. $\frac{9^2 - 11}{(3 + 4) \cdot 10}$ **1**
14. $\frac{3^2 - 4 \cdot 3 + 4}{3^2 - 4}$ **√5**
15. $\frac{3 \cdot 2 + 6 + 2 \cdot 3 + 6}{3^2 + 2^2 + 1^2}$ **1/7**
16. $\frac{2 \cdot 4 - 6(2 + 1)}{1^2 - 3 \cdot 2}$ **2**
17. $\frac{(4 - 6)^2}{-24 + 12}$ **-2**
18. $\frac{2 \cdot 6 - (4 + 2)}{(-2 - 4 - 6) + (2 - 1)}$ **-½**
19. $\frac{-3(4 - 9)}{35 \div -7}$ **-3**
20. $3^5 \div 3^2 + 3^2 + 3$ **1**

Page 5

84 Operations with Real Numbers
Opposites and Absolute Values

$-(5c + 9d) = -5c - 9d$ $-|7 - 9| = -|-2| = -2$

1. $|-12|$ **12**
2. $-|5\frac{1}{2}|$ **-5½**
3. $|-5| + |9|$ **14**
4. $7 + |-3|$ **10**
5. $|7| + |-7|$ **14**
6. $-(-3 + 4)$ **-1**
7. $-(9 - 9)$ **0**
8. $|9| - |-12|$ **-3**
9. $|-3| + |9| - 6$ **6**
10. $-3 |5| - |5|$ **-20**
11. $|-25| - |-14|$ **11**
12. $-18 + (-(-13))$ **-5**
13. $|1 - 3| + 5$ **7**
14. $\frac{-|-3 + 5|}{-9 + (-(-1))}$ **¼**
15. $-(2n - (-7))$ **-2n-7**
16. $-(-2x + -3y)$ **2x+3y**
17. $-(6x - 4y)$ **-6x + 4y**
18. $10m - (-2n)$ **10m + 2n**
19. $-2(3m^2 - 2m - 1)$ **-6m²+4m +2**
20. $-3(4x - 6y)$ **-12x + 18y**

Page 6

Operations with Real Numbers 84
Real Numbers: Preparing for College

1. $1 - 3$ equals
   a. -4   (b. -2)   c. 4   d. 2

2. If x and y are positive integers and if $\frac{x}{y} = 1$ and $(x + y)^2 = z$, which of the following can equal z?
   a. 5   b. 9   (c. 16)   d. 25

3. $(-1)(-2)(-3)(+4) =$
   a. -10   b. 24   (c. -24)   d. -36

4. $(-2) - (-5) =$
   a. -7   b. -3   (c. 3)   d. 7

5. $(-5) + (-2) =$
   (a. -7)   b. -3   c. 3   d. 7

6. $(\frac{1}{2}) + (-\frac{7}{8}) =$
   (a. -$\frac{4}{7}$)   b. -$\frac{7}{16}$ c. -1$\frac{3}{4}$ d. -2$\frac{2}{7}$

7. $7 - ((-8) + (-2)) =$
   a. -3   b. -1   c. 13   (d. 17)

8. $\left| \frac{(-18) + (-2)}{(7) + (-2)} \right|$ a. 2$\frac{2}{9}$ (b. 4)   c. 3$\frac{1}{5}$ d. -4

9. The integers -2, -7, 5 and -5 written from least to greatest are:
   a. -2, -5, -7, 5   b. -5, -7, -2, 5   (c. -7, -5, -2, 5)   d. -7, -2, -5, 5

10. Which of the following conditions will make x – y a negative number?
    (a. y > x)   b. x > y   c. y > 0   d. x = y

Page 7

Variables and Equations

☞ Keep in mind...
Triumph = Umph! added to Try

Combining Like Terms

$8x + 5y + -17x = -9x + 5y$

1. $9x + 4x$ **13x**
2. $17x + x$ **18x**
3. $m + (-4m)$ **-3m**
4. $-7x - 8x$ **-15x**
5. $14a - 19a$ **-5a**
6. $-a + 9a$ **8a**
7. $6xy + 5xy$ **11xy**
8. $-9m - m$ **-10m**
9. $15a + (-11a)$ **4a**
10. $-14x + 13x$ **-x**
11. $5x^2y + 13x^2y$ **18x²y**
12. $21xy + (-9yx)$ **12xy**
13. $17x + 1$ **17x+1**
14. $3.5y - 7.2y$ **-3.7y**
15. $-4.7y - 2.3y$ **-7y**
16. $3a + 5c - 9a$ **-6a + 5c**
17. $2x - 9x + 7$ **-7x +7**
18. $7x - 8 - 11x$ **-4x-8**
19. $3x - 3y - 9x + 7y$ **-6x +4y**
20. $17x + 4 - 3x$ **14x +4**
21. $3x - 7y - 12y$ **3x-19y**
22. $11a - 13a + 15a$ **13a**
23. $17x + 5a - 3x - 4a$ **14x + a**
24. $6x + 9y + 2x - 8y + 5$ **8x+y +5**
25. $3xy + 4yx + 5x^2y + 6xy^2$ **7xy+5x²y+6xy²**
26. $-25y - 17y + 6xy - 3xy$ **-42y+3xy**

Page 8

104

© MCMXCIV Instructional Fair, Inc.

Answer Key

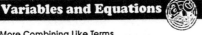

Variables and Equations

...More Combining Like Terms

$$3(a+2)+(2a-6b)=3a+6+2a-6b=5a-6b+6$$

1. $5t+3r+9t-10r-8$
$14t-7r-8$

2. $4a+(-2b)+(-2a)+b$
$2a-b$

3. $12x-3y+x+2y$
$13x-y$

4. $-30x-(-1x)$
$-29x$

5. $6(x-y)-3(3x+y)$
$-3x-9y$

6. $17x+3y+30x-5y$
$47x-2y$

7. $4p-6q+6q-10p+q$
$-6p+q$

8. $-r+7+3r-9-2r$
-2

9. $8(x+y)+3(x-y)$
$11x+5y$

10. $3(x+7y)-5(x+7y)+9(x+7y)$
$7(x+y)$ or $7x+49y$

11. $2(-2a^2-4d)-(-3a^2+17d)$
$-a^2-25d$

12. $2(3(-x^2+x)-1)-5x+6x^2$
$x-2$

13. $3(a+2b)+-(b+2a)$
$a+5b$

14. $-5(a-b)-(a-b)+8(a-b)$
$2a-2b$

15. $-4(x+5(-3xy+x))-(10+15xy)$
$45xy-24x-10$

16. $\frac{5}{8}c^2-\frac{1}{4}-\frac{3}{7}c^2+\frac{3}{5}d$
$\frac{11}{56}c^2+\frac{7}{20}d$

17. $3\cdot5a-7\cdot3b-3\cdot2a+2\cdot9b$
$9a-3b$

18. $2\frac{1}{2}xy-xy+3\frac{1}{3}xy$
$4\frac{5}{6}xy$

19. $6(x^2+y^2)-7(x^2+y^2)$
$-x^2-y^2$

20. $4x-y+2\frac{1}{2}x+3\frac{1}{4}y$
$6\frac{1}{2}x+2\frac{1}{4}y$

Page 9

Variables and Equations

Solving Equations with Addition and Subtraction

$$16+x=-14$$
$$16+-16+x=-14+-16$$
$$x=-30$$

1. $x+7=-13$ -20

2. $x+7=4$ $x=-3$

3. $-14+y=-17$ $y=-3$

4. $y-11=14$ $y=25$

5. $y-5=-7$ $y=-2$

6. $-20+x=-80$ $x=-60$

7. $6+x=29$ $x=23$

8. $a+32=-4$ $a=-36$

9. $-2=x-2$ $x=0$

10. $-19+y=42$ $y=61$

11. $16=z-10$ $z=26$

12. $y+73=0$ $y=-73$

13. $-100=b+(-72)$ $b=-28$

14. $w-5=(8-13)$ $w=0$

15. $x+2.5=-4.7$ $x=-7.2$

16. $a+3.6=-.2$ $a=-3.8$

17. $x-6\frac{1}{4}=12\frac{1}{2}$ $x=18\frac{3}{4}$

18. $2\frac{1}{5}+x=-3\frac{1}{2}$ $x=-5\frac{7}{10}$

19. $n+\frac{1}{2}=\frac{3}{4}$ $n=\frac{1}{4}$

20. $b-1\frac{1}{3}=-3\frac{5}{6}$ $b=-2\frac{1}{2}$

Page 10

Variables and Equations

Solving Equations with Multiplication and Division

$$2x=12$$
$$\frac{2x}{2}=\frac{12}{2}$$
$$x=6$$

$$-\frac{3}{4}y=15$$
$$-\frac{4}{3}\cdot-\frac{3}{4}y=15\cdot-\frac{4}{3}$$
$$y=-20$$

1. $3x=-21$ $x=-7$

2. $-7y=28$ $y=-4$

3. $-28=-196x$ $x=\frac{1}{7}$

4. $-15a=-45$ $a=3$

5. $-x=17$ $x=-17$

6. $-21=-2x$ $x=10\frac{1}{2}$

7. $-12b=-288$ $b=24$

8. $12x=-60$ $x=-5$

9. $\frac{a}{5}=-6$ $a=-30$

10. $-\frac{2}{5}y=-14$ $y=35$

11. $\frac{3x}{4}=-24$ $x=-32$

12. $-\frac{x}{3}=\frac{4}{9}$ $x=-1\frac{1}{3}$

13. $-\frac{3}{7}=\frac{a}{14}$ $a=-6$

14. $3a=-\frac{1}{4}$ $a=-\frac{1}{12}$

15. $\frac{a}{2.4}=.26$ $a=.624$

16. $-\frac{1}{99}y=0$ $y=0$

17. $-1.5x=6$ $x=-4$

18. $-12.5=4n$ $n=-3.125$

19. $-3.7w=-11.1$ $w=3$

20. $\frac{y}{6}=-\frac{2}{3}$ $y=-4$

Page 11

Variables and Equations

Solving Basic Combined Equations

$$7(x+2)=-35$$
$$7x+14=-35$$
$$7x+14-14=-35-14$$
$$\frac{7x}{7}=\frac{-49}{7}$$
$$x=-7$$

1. $5x-3=22$ $x=5$

2. $4a+3=-5$ $a=-2$

3. $5-7y=33$ $y=-4$

4. $5x-11=-16$ $x=-1$

5. $-3=5x+12$ $x=-3$

6. $0=.6x-3.6$ $x=6$

7. $6-8x=-26$ $x=4$

8. $5=5x+27$ $x=-4\frac{2}{5}$

9. $3(w+3)=-15$ $x=-8$

10. $2(y+1)-5=7$ $y=5$

11. $6-\frac{2}{3}x=-8$ $x=21$

12. $.3x-4.2=2.7$ $x=23$

13. $8.6=2.1-1.3y$ $y=-5$

14. $5-4(y+1)=-3$ $y=1$

15. $-1=\frac{y}{4}-6$ $y=-20$

16. $\frac{5x}{6}+34=9$ $x=-30$

17. $\frac{2}{3}d+3=11$ $d=-12$

18. $1.2x+6=-1.2$ $x=-6$

19. $28=\frac{17}{32}x-23$ $x=96$

20. $\frac{2x}{5}+4=-12$ $x=-40$

Page 12

Answer Key

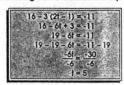

Variables and Equations

...More Solving Basic Combined Equations

$$16 - 3(2t - 1) = -11$$
$$16 - 6t + 3 = -11$$
$$19 - 6t = -11$$
$$19 - 19 - 6t = -11 - 19$$
$$\frac{-6t}{-6} = \frac{-30}{-6}$$
$$t = 5$$

1. $y - 16 - 3y = 0$ $\quad y = -8$

2. $z - 4 - 4z = -1$ $\quad z = -1$

3. $6x - 2x = -64$ $\quad x = -16$

4. $8y + 4 - 2y = 22$ $\quad y = 3$

5. $12 = 3x - x + 4x$ $\quad x = 2$

6. $2(x - 3) - x = -1$ $\quad x = 5$

7. $3(y - 4) = 15$ $\quad y = 9$

8. $3x - 2(x + 4) = 8$ $\quad x = 16$

9. $2(y - 1) - y = -2$ $\quad y = 0$

10. $5(2a - 2) + 4 = 4$ $\quad a = 1$

11. $3(b + 2) + 2(b - 3) = -5$ $\quad b = -1$

12. $4x - 2(x - 5) = -2$ $\quad x = -6$

13. $4a - (a + 6) = 12 - 36$ $\quad a = -6$

14. $6x - (x + 7) = 13 - 5$ $\quad x = 3$

15. $3n + 3(1 - n) - n = -6$ $\quad n = 9$

16. $7x - 2(x + 6) = 3$ $\quad x = 3$

17. $\frac{6n}{8} + 12 = 84$ $\quad n = 96$

18. $-2(-3 - 4x) = -10$ $\quad x = -2$

19. $2x + 3(x - 9) - 2(x + 3) = 0$ $\quad x = 11$

20. $-6x + 9 + 4x = -3$ $\quad x = 6$

Page 13

Variables and Equations

Solving Equations with Variables on Both Sides

$$4x - 6 = x + 9$$
$$4x - x - 6 = x - x + 9$$
$$3x - 6 = 9$$
$$3x - 6 + 6 = 9 + 6$$
$$\frac{3x}{3} = \frac{15}{3}$$
$$x = 5$$

1. $4x - 6 = x + a$ $\quad x = 5$

2. $4 - 7x = 1 - 6x$ $\quad x = 3$

3. $-4x - 3 = -6x + 9$ $\quad x = 6$

4. $41 - 2n = 2 + n$ $\quad n = 13$

5. $6(2 + y) = 3(3 - y)$ $\quad y = -\frac{1}{3}$

6. $4y = 2(y - 5) - 2$ $\quad y = -6$

7. $6x - 9x - 4 = -2x - 2$ $\quad x = -2$

8. $-(x + 7) = -6x + 8$ $\quad x = 3$

9. $3 - 6a = 9 - 5a$ $\quad a = -6$

10. $-9x + 6 = -x + 4$ $\quad x = \frac{1}{4}$

11. $5x - 7 = -10x + 8$ $\quad x = 1$

12. $7y + 3 = 4y - 18$ $\quad y = -7$

13. $-3(y + 3) = 2y + 3$ $\quad y = -2\frac{2}{5}$

14. $2(-3a + 5) = -4(a + 4)$ $\quad a = 13$

15. $7x - 3 = 2(x + 6)$ $\quad x = 3$

16. $-6x + 9 = 4(5 - x)$ $\quad x = -5\frac{1}{2}$

17. $3(x + 2) = -5 - 2(x - 3)$ $\quad x = -1$

18. $2(x - 3) = (x - 1) + 7$ $\quad x = 12$

19. $\frac{1}{3}(6y - 9) = -2y + 13$ $\quad y = 4$

20. $\frac{1}{6}(12 - 6x) = 5(x + 4)$ $\quad x = -3$

Page 14

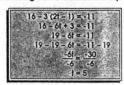

Variables and Equations

Solving Equations: the Big Picture

The Process

1. Is it a subtraction problem?
   - no →
   - yes → Change it to an addition sentence.
2. Are there grouping symbols?
   - no →
   - yes → Distribute.
3. Are there variables on the right side?
   - no →
   - yes → Move them to the left side.
   - combine/simplify left side
4. Is there a number *not* attached to the variable?
   - no →
   - yes → Move it to the right side (combine).
5. Is there a number attached to the variable?
   - no →
   - yes →
     1. if by ⊗ → then ÷
     2. if by ÷ → then ⊗
     3. if a fraction → then use reciprocal
   - variable = #
   - variable = #

Using the chart above solve these problems by asking each question.

1. $3(x - 5) = 21$ $\quad x = 12$

2. $x + 9 = 4x - 6$ $\quad x = 5$

3. $-6 + 2x = 9 - 3x$ $\quad x = 3$

4. $-6x + 9 = -4x - 3$ $\quad x = 6$

Page 15

Variables and Equations

Equations, the Big Picture...Putting It All Together

1. $\frac{3}{2}x - 9 = 0$ $\quad x = 6$

2. $6x + 3 = -5x + 14$ $\quad x = 1$

3. $\frac{1}{8}x + 3 = 2$ $\quad x = -8$

4. $5y = 2y - 42 - 3y$ $\quad y = -7$

5. $37 + 8x = 4(7 - x)$ $\quad x = -\frac{3}{4}$

6. $5(2 - x) = 7x - 26$ $\quad x = 3$

7. $6 + 4x = \frac{1}{3}(6x + 9)$ $\quad x = -\frac{3}{2}$

8. $1.6(3y - 1) + 2 = 5y$ $\quad y = 2$

9. $7x - 10 = 6(11 - 2x)$ $\quad x = 4$

10. $3(4x - 9) = 5(2x - 5)$ $\quad x = 1$

11. $\frac{3}{4}(x + 7) = x + 50$ $\quad x = -179$

12. $\frac{5}{7}y - 15 = 5y + 30$ $\quad y = -10\frac{1}{2}$

Page 16

Answer Key

Variables and Equations
Problem Solving Using Equations

Set up and solve each equation.

> The sum of twice a number and 21 is 83. Find the number.
> $2n + 21 = 83$
> $2n + 21 - 21 = 83 - 21$
> $2n = 62$
> $n = 31$
> The number is 31.

1. Twice a number, diminished by 17 is -3. Find the number. **7**

2. Six times a number, increased by 3 is 27. Find the number. **4**

3. Three times the difference of 5 minus a number is 27. Find the number. **-4**

4. Karl's team score is 39 points. This was one point less than twice Todd's team score. Find Todd's team score. **20**

5. The length of a rectangle is 6 feet more than twice the width. If the length is 24 feet, what is the width? **9 feet**

6. Four-fifths of the third grade went on a trip to the zoo. If 64 children made the trip, how many children are in the third grade? **80**

7. The price of a pack of gum today is 63¢. This is 3¢ more than three times the price ten years ago. What was the price ten years ago? **20¢**

8. The sum of three consecutive integers is 279. Find the integers. **92, 93, 94**

9. The sum of two consecutive odd integers is 112. Find the integers. **55, 57**

10. Find four consecutive integers such that the sum of the second and fourth is 132. **64, 65, 66, 67**

11. Find three consecutive odd integers such that their sum decreased by the second equals 50. **23, 25, 27**

Page 17

Variables and Equations
...More Problem Solving Using Equations

Set up and solve each equation.

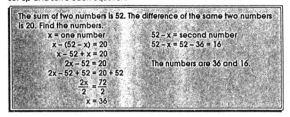

> The sum of two numbers is 52. The difference of the same two numbers is 20. Find the numbers.
> x = one number $52 - x$ = second number
> $x - (52 - x) = 20$ $52 - x = 52 - 36 = 16$
> $x - 52 + x = 20$
> $2x - 52 = 20$ The numbers are 36 and 16.
> $2x - 52 + 52 = 20 + 52$
> $\frac{2x}{2} = \frac{72}{2}$
> $x = 36$

1. One number is four times another. Their sum is 35. Find the numbers. **7, 28**

2. The sum of two numbers is 21. On number is three less than the other. Find the numbers. **9, 12**

3. The greater of two numbers is one less than 8 times the smaller. Their sum is 98. Find the numbers. **11, 87**

4. In a triangle, the second angle measures twice the first, and the third angle measures 5 more than the second. If the sum of the angles' measures is 180°, find the measure of each angle. **35°, 70°, 75°**

5. The length of a rectangle is 4 centimeters (cm) less than three times the width. The perimeter is 64 cm. Find the width and length.
(Hint: Perimeter = 2l + 2w) **w = 9, l = 23**

6. The sum of three numbers is 64. The second number is 3 more than the first. The third number is 11 less than twice the first. Find the numbers. **18, 21, 25**

7. Bill can type 19 words per minute faster than Bob. Their combined typing speed is 97 words per minute. Find Bob's typing speed. **39**

Page 18

Variables and Equations
Equations and Problem Solving Summary

1. $6y = 10 + 4y$ **y = 5**

2. $-27 - 6a = 3a$ **a = -3**

3. $10x + 6 = 12x - 18$ **x = 12**

4. $8x - (6x - 4) = 10$ **x = 3**

5. $3(x + 5) = 27$ **x = 4**

6. $4(n - 7) = 2n - 8$ **n = 10**

7. $3x - (x + 4) = -x + 8$ **x = 4**

8. $3(2y + 4) = 4(y + 7)$ **y = 8**

9. $2(5x - 3) = 3(2x + 2)$ **x = 3**

10. $4(a - 5) + 4a = 2(3a + 4)$ **a = 14**

11. One number is 5 more than another. Five times the smaller equals 4 times the larger. Find the numbers. **20, 25**

12. One number is 6 less than another. Three times the smaller is 2 more than twice the larger. Find the numbers. **14, 20**

13. Bill has twice as much money as Bob. Paul has $12 more than Bill. Together they have $92. How much money does Bob have? **$16**

14. Find two consecutive whole numbers that total 93. **46, 47**

15. The Colts played 76 games. They won 3 times as many games as they lost. How many did they win? **57 games**

Page 19

Variables and Equations
Basic Inequalities: Solve and Graph

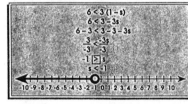

> $6 < 3(1 - s)$
> $6 < 3 - 3s$
> $6 - 3 < 3 - 3 - 3s$
> $\frac{3}{-3} < \frac{-3s}{-3}$
> $-1 > s$
> $s < -1$

1. $x + 4 > 12$ **x > 8**

2. $32 > -4(4y)$ **y > -2**

3. $3y + 1 < 13$ **y < 4**

4. $10\frac{1}{2} < 2z + 18\frac{1}{2}$ **z > -4**

5. $2 - \frac{n}{3} < -1$ **n > 9**

6. $-2x - 5 > 6$ **x < -5\frac{1}{2}**

7. $-3m + 6(m - 2) > 9$ **m > 7**

8. $15x - 2 < 3x - 11$ **x < -\frac{3}{4}**

9. $2(t + 3) < 3(t + 2)$ **t > 0**

10. $15x - 2(x - 4) > 3$ **x > -\frac{5}{13}**

11. $x - 1.5 < .5(x + 4)$ **x < 7**

12. $-3(2m - 8) < 2(m + 14)$ **m > \frac{1}{2}**

13. $2x + 3 < 6x - 1$ **x > 1**

14. $3x - 2 \geq 7x - 10$ **x ≤ 2**

Page 20

Answer Key

Compound Inequalities: Solve and Graph

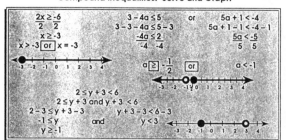

1. $t \le -1$ or $t \le -3$

2. $-2 \le x \le 6$

3. $x + 1 \le -3$ or $x + 1 \ge 3$ $x \ge 2$ $x \le -4$

4. $-2 < 3t - 2 < 10$ $0 < t < 4$

5. $-(x - 2) \ge 3$ $x \le -1$

6. $3x - 7 < 11$ or $9x - 4 > x + 4$
$x < 6$ or $x > 1$

7. $-6 \le -2z \le 4$ $-2 \le z \le 3$

8. $9 \le 2a + 5 < 15$ $2 \le a < 5$

9. $3 < 2x + 1 < 7$ $1 < x < 3$

10. $-8 < 2x + 4 \le -2$ $-6 < x \le -3$

11. $-6 \le 3 - 2(x + 4) \le 3$ $-4 < x \le \frac{1}{2}$

12. $4 - 3x \le -8$ or $3x - 1 \le 8$ $x \le 3$ or $x \ge 4$

☞ Keep in mind...
A person who makes no mistakes does not usually make anything.
E. Phelps

Exponents

I. Write in exponential form.

| $4 \cdot x \cdot x \cdot y \cdot y \cdot y = 4x^3y^3$ | The cube of $c - 4 = (c - 4)^3$ |

1. $a \cdot a \cdot a \cdot b$ a^3b

2. $mn \cdot mn \cdot mn \cdot mn$ $(mn)^4$

3. $9 \cdot x \cdot x \cdot x \cdot x \cdot y \cdot y \cdot z$ $9x^5y^2z$

4. $5(c + 1)(c + 1)(c + 1)$ $5(c+1)^3$

5. $(a + b)$ squared $(a+b)^2$

6. The quotient of 3 and the cube of $y + 2$ $\frac{3}{(y+2)^3}$

7. $x \cdot x \cdot y \cdot y \cdot y \cdot y \cdot z$ x^2y^4z

8. $(-x)(-x)(-x)$ $(-x)^3$

9. $3 \cdot ab \cdot ab \cdot ab \cdot ab$ $3(ab)^4$ or $3a^4b^4$

10. The square of $x^2y - 3$ $(x^2y-3)^2$

II. Evaluate each expression if $x = -1$, $y = 2$, $z = -3$

| $5x^2z^2 = 5 \cdot x \cdot x \cdot z \cdot z = 5 \cdot -1 \cdot -1 \cdot -3 \cdot -3 = 45$ |

1. x^5 -1

2. x^2yz -6

3. $4y^3z$ -96

4. $x^5y^2z^3$ 432

5. $-(xyz)$ -6

6. $10z^5$ -2430

7. x^3yz^2 18

8. $-2xy^2$ 8

9. $\frac{xz^2}{z}$ -3

10. $11x^2$ 11

Adding and Subtracting Polynomials

| $(x^3 + 2x^2 - 8x) - (-2x^2 + 7x - 5) = x^3 + 2x^2 - 8x + 2x^2 - 7x + 5 = x^3 + 4x^2 - 15x + 5$ |

1. $(4x + 2) + (x - 1)$ $5x+1$

2. $(5a - 2b + 4) + (2a + b + 2)$ $7a+b+6$

3. $(3a + 2b) - (a - b)$ $2a+b$

4. $(x^2 + y^2 - ab) - (x^2 - y^2 + ab)$ $2y^2-2ab$

5. $(4a^2 - 5ab - 6b^2) + (10ab - 6a^2 - 8b^2)$ $-2a^2 + 5ab - 14b^2$

6. $(4x^2 - 2x - 3) - (-5x - 4)$ $4x^2 + 3x + 1$

7. $(4a^2 - 4ab - b^2) + (a^2 - b^2) + (2ab + a^2 + b^2)$ $6a^2 - 2ab - b^2$

8. $(-4x^3 - 6x^2 + 3x - 1) - (8x^3 + 4x^2 - 2x + 3)$ $-12x^3 - 10x^2 + 5x - 4$

9. $(a + 2b) + (3b - 4c) + (5a - 7c) + 3b$ $6a + 8b - 11c$

10. $(x^2 - 2xy + y^2) - (x^2 - 2xy + y^2)$ 0

11. $(x + 3y) + (-3x - y) - (x - y)$ $-3x + 3y$

12. $(2x^2 + 3y^2 - z^2) - (x^2 - y^2 - z^2) + (4x^2 - 3y^2)$ $5x^2 + y^2$

13. $(2x + 3) + (-2x^2 + x - 5)$ $-2x^2 + 3x - 2$

14. $(2y + 3x - 4) + (9 - 8y - 5x) + (3x + 4y - 2)$ $x - 2y + 3$

15. $(-2y^2 + 8) - (3y^2 - 4y - 6)$ $-5y^2 + 4y + 14$

16. $(7y + 4x + 9) - (6x - 8y + 11)$ $-2x + 15y - 2$

Find the perimeter.

17.

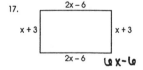
$6x - 6$

18.

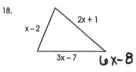
$6x - 8$

Multiplying with Monomials

| $(3a^2b)(5a^2b) = 3 \cdot 5a^{2+2}b^{1+1} = 15a^4b^2$ |
| $(-2a^2b)^4 = (-2)^4(a^2)^4(b)^4 = -2 \cdot -2 \cdot -2 \cdot -2 \cdot a^2 \cdot 4 b^{1 \cdot 4} = 16a^8b^4$ |

1. $(4c)^2$ $16c^2$

2. $(2a^2b)(4ab^2)$ $8a^3b^3$

3. $(4pq)(-p^2q^3)$ $-4p^3q^4$

4. $2x(-xy)(-y^2)$ $2x^2y^3$

5. $a(2a^2)^3$ $8a^7$

6. $3s(-2st)$ $12s^3t^2$

7. $(-xy^2)^3(2x^2y)^2$ $-4x^7y^8$

8. $x^2(-2xz)(4z^3)$ $-8x^3z^6$

9. $(3pq^2r^3)(\frac{1}{3}q^2t)$ pq^4r^4

10. $(-x)(-2xy)(-3xyz)$ $-6x^3y^2z$

11. $2x^2(xy^2)^2(xz^2)^2$ $2x^6y^4z^4$

12. $(2u)^2(u^3v)^3(w)$ $4u^8v^3w$

13. $(-x)(-x^5)$ x^6

14. $(-5x^2)(7xy^3)$ $-35x^3y^3$

15. $(-x^3y)(6xy^3)(3x^2y^2)$ $-18x^6y^6$

16. $(-4rt^2)(2rt)(-t^2)$ $8r^2t^5$

17. $(-3ab)(-3ab^2)(-3a^2b^3)$ $-27a^4b^6$

18. $-1(-4x^2)(5x^6)$ $20x^8$

Multiply, then add or subtract.

19. $(2a)(3a^3) + (2a^2)(a^2)$ $8a^4$

20. $(a^2b)(2a^2b^3) - (a^2b)(-3a^2b^3)$ $5a^4b^4$

21. $a^2(ab^3)^2 + b^2(a^2b^2)^2$ $2a^4b^4$

22. $(r^2s)^3(rs^2)^2 - r(-rs)^7$ $2r^8s^7$

Polynomials

Multiplying a Polynomial by a Monomial

$-2a^2(9-a-4a^2) = -2a^2 \cdot 9 - (-2a^2 \cdot a) - (-2a^2 \cdot 4a^2) = -18a^2 + 2a^3 + 8a^4$
$(x+2)(2x^2) = 2x^2 \cdot x + 2x^2 \cdot 2 = 2x^3 + 4x^2$

1. $2(x^2 - xy + 3y^2)$ $2x^2 - 2xy + 6y^2$
2. $-2n(4 + 5n^3)$ $-8n - 10n^4$
3. $c^2d(c^2d^3 + 2cd^2 + d)$ $c^4d^4 + 2c^3d^3 + c^2d^2$
4. $2xy^2(2 - x - x^2y)$ $4xy^2 - 2x^2y^2 - 2x^3y^3$
5. $(a^2 - 3ab - 2b^2)(-2ab)$ $-2a^3b + 6a^2b^2 + 4ab^3$
6. $3n(8n^2 - 2n)$ $24n^3 - 6n^2$
7. $(w^2z - 2wz + z)(-z^2)$ $-w^2z^3 + 2wz^3 - z^3$
8. $-3ab^2(a^3b^2 - 2a^2b)$ $-3a^4b^4 + 6a^3b^3$
9. $4x^3y(9x^2 - 6xy^2 - 7)$ $36x^5y - 24x^4y^3 - 28x^3y$
10. $-6k^2m^2(2k - 3m + 4km - k^2m^2)$ $-12k^3m^2 + 18k^2m^3 - 24k^3m^3 + 6k^4m^4$
11. $-n^2(n + 4n^2)$ $-4n^4 - n^3$
12. $(4x^2 - 7x)(-x)$ $-4x^3 + 7x^2$
13. $2x^2(x^3 - 2x^2 + 8x - 5)$ $2x^5 - 4x^4 + 16x^3 - 10x^2$
14. $(-6x^2)(3x^2 - 1)$ $-18x^5 + 6x^3$
15. $(6x - 5x^2 + 8)(-3x)$ $15x^3 - 18x^2 - 24x$
16. $-5x^2(2x^3 + 3x^2 - 7x + 9)$ $-10x^5 - 15x^4 + 35x^3 - 45x^2$

Find the area.

$A = l \cdot w$

17.

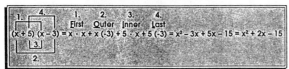
$x + 4$; $2x$; $a = 2x^2 + 8x$

18. A triangle has a base length (b) of $2x + 4$ and a height (h) of $3y$.

(Area $= \frac{1}{2}bh$) $3xy + 6y$

Polynomials

Multiplying Polynomials

$(s-2)(s^2 - s + 3) = s(s^2 - s + 3) - 2(s^2 - s + 3)$
$= s \cdot s^2 - s \cdot s + s \cdot 3 - 2 \cdot s^2 - 2 \cdot (-s) - 2 \cdot 3$
$= s^3 - s^2 + 3s - 2s^2 + 2s - 6$
$= s^3 - 3s^2 + 5s - 6$

1. $(z-3)(z+3)$ $z^2 - 9$
2. $(3t-2)(t-3)$ $4t^2 - 11t + 6$
3. $(a+5)(a+5)$ $a^2 + 10a + 25$
4. $(a+b)(2x+y)$ $2ax + 2bx + ay + by$
5. $(\frac{1}{2}x - y)(2x + y)$ $x^2 - \frac{3}{2}xy - y^2$
6. $(4x-5)(4x+5)$ $16x^2 - 25$
7. $(1.6n - 9)(.2n - 5)$ $32n^2 - 9.8n + 45$
8. $(2c + d)(c^2 + 2c + 2d)$ $2c^3 + 4c^2 + 6cd + c^2d + 2d^2$
9. $(3a^2 - 2b^2)(3a^2 + 2b^2)$ $9a^4 - 4b^4$
10. $(h + k)(h^2 - 2hk + 3k^2)$ $h^3 - h^2k + hk^2 + 3k^3$
11. $(2x-1)(x^2 + x + 3)$ $2x^3 + x^2 + 5x - 3$
12. $(x^3 + 3x^2 + 2x - 1)(x - 1)$ $x^4 + 2x^3 - x^2 - 3x + 1$
13. $(n - m)(n^2 + m^2)$ $-m^3 + m^2n - mn^2 + n^3$
14. $(y + 1)(y^2 - 2y + 2)$ $y^3 - y^2 + 2$
15. $(\frac{1}{3}x - 2)(\frac{1}{2}x + 6)$ $\frac{1}{6}x^2 + x - 12$
16. $(3x^2 - 4x - 7)(x + 5)$ $3x^3 + 11x^2 - 27x - 35$
17. $(x^2 - 3)(2x^2 + 3x + 5)$ $2x^4 + 3x^3 - x^2 - 9x - 15$
18. $(4x^2 - 6x + 4)(3x + 2)$ $12x^3 - 10x^2 + 8$

Polynomials

Multiplying Binomials Using FOIL

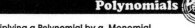

First Outer Inner Last
$(x+5)(x-3) = x \cdot x + x \cdot (-3) + 5 \cdot x + 5 \cdot (-3) = x^2 - 3x + 5x - 15 = x^2 + 2x - 15$

1. $(x+2)(x+3)$ $x^2 + 5x + 6$
2. $(y+7)(y+4)$ $y^2 + 11y + 28$
3. $(x-8)(x+4)$ $x^2 - 4x - 32$
4. $(x-8)(x-4)$ $x^2 - 12x + 32$
5. $(y-4)(y+5)$ $y^2 + y - 20$
6. $(x-9)(x-2)$ $x^2 - 11x + 18$
7. $(2x+4)(x+3)$ $2x^2 + 10x + 12$
8. $(3x+2)(2x+5)$ $6x^2 + 19x + 10$
9. $(4x-9)(3x+1)$ $12x^2 - 23x - 9$
10. $(2x+5)(4x-3)$ $8x^2 + 14x - 15$
11. $(n-7)(3n-2)$ $3n^2 - 23n + 14$
12. $(5x+2)(3x-7)$ $15x^2 - 29x - 14$
13. $(-4x+5)(-2x-3)$ $8x^2 + 2x - 15$
14. $(-x-4)(4+3x)$ $-3x^2 - 16x - 16$
15. $(x+2y)(2x+3y)$ $2x^2 + 7xy + 6y^2$
16. $(6x-y)(3x-2y)$ $18x^2 - 15xy + 2y^2$
17. $(4x+y)(3x-4y)$ $12x^2 - 13xy - 4y^2$
18. $(5a+3b)(4a-b)$ $20a^2 + 7ab - 3b^2$

Polynomials

...More Multiplying Binomials Using FOIL

$(x+3)(x-4) = x^2 - 4x + 3x - 12 = x^2 - x - 12$

1. $(n-7)(n-2)$ $n^2 - 9n + 14$
2. $(6-t)(3+t)$ $18 + 3t - t^2$
3. $(3r+2)(r-4)$ $3r^2 - 10r - 8$
4. $(4u-3)(3u+2)$ $12u^2 - u - 6$
5. $(\frac{1}{2}x+5)(6x-10)$ $3x^2 + 25x - 50$
6. $(x+y)(x+2y)$ $x^2 + 3xy + 2y^2$
7. $(3r+s)(2r-3s)$ $6r^2 - 7rs - 3s^2$
8. $(.3x - .4)(.5x - .1)$ $.15x^2 - .23x + .04$
9. $(7m-n)(m-7n)$ $7m^2 - 50mn + 7n^2$
10. $(4b-3c)(4b+3c)$ $16b^2 - 9c^2$
11. $(a^2 - 3b)(a^2 + 2b)$ $a^4 - a^2b - 6b^2$
12. $(8x + \frac{2}{3})(6x + \frac{3}{2})$ $48x^2 + 16x + 1$
13. $(r^2 - 2s)(2r^2 + s)$ $2r^4 - 3r^2s - 2s^2$
14. $(\frac{1}{2}x + 3)(4x + 5)$ $2x^2 + \frac{29}{2}x + 15$
15. $(x+5)(x^2 + 4x)$ $x^3 + 9x^2 + 20x$
16. $(2x^2 - 6x)(7x + 1)$ $14x^3 - 40x^2 - 6x$
17. $(2x-1)(6x-7)$ $12x^2 - 20x + 7$
18. $(4x-1)(8x^2 + 3)$ $32x^3 - 8x^2 + 12x - 3$
19. $(5x-2)(-x-5)$ $-5x^2 - 23x + 10$
20. $(x - \frac{1}{2})(2x - \frac{1}{3})$ $2x^2 - \frac{4}{3}x + \frac{1}{6}$

Answer Key

Special Products

$$(2x + 5)(2x - 5) = 4x^2 - 10x + 10x - 25 = 4x^2 - 25$$

1. $(x + 3)(x - 3)$
$x^2 - 9$

2. $(y - 10)(y + 10)$
$y^2 - 100$

3. $(a + 4)(a - 4)$
$a^2 - 16$

4. $(x + 7)(x - 7)$
$x^2 - 49$

5. $(2x + 1)(2x - 1)$
$4x^2 - 1$

6. $(2x - 3)(2x + 3)$
$4x^2 - 9$

7. $(5x - 6)(5x + 6)$
$25x^2 - 36$

8. $(4x + 3)(4x - 3)$
$16x^2 - 9$

9. $(3x + 3)(3x - 3)$
$9x^2 - 9$

10. $(3n + 4)(3n - 4)$
$9n^2 - 16$

11. $(2x + 9)(2x - 9)$
$4x^2 - 81$

12. $(7x - 5)(7x + 5)$
$49x^2 - 25$

13. $(x + y)(x - y)$
$x^2 - y^2$

14. $(5x - y)(5x + y)$
$25x^2 - y^2$

15. $(2x - 5y)(2x + 5y)$
$4x^2 - 25y^2$

16. $(3x - 7y)(3x + 7y)$
$9x^2 - 49y^2$

17. $(2x + 11y)(2x - 11y)$
$4x^2 - 121y^2$

18. $(b - a)(b + a)$
$b^2 - a^2$

19. $(2x + y^2)(2x - y^2)$
$4x^2 - y^4$

20. $(7n^2 + 8)(7n^2 - 8)$
$49n^4 - 64$

Page 29

Squaring Binomials

$$(a + b)^2 = (a + b)(a + b) = a^2 + ab + ab + b^2 = a^2 + 2ab + b^2$$

1. $(x - 8)^2$
$x^2 - 16x + 64$

2. $(a + 5)^2$
$a^2 + 10a + 25$

3. $(x - 3)^2$
$x^2 - 6x + 9$

4. $(3n + 1)^2$
$9n^2 + 6n + 1$

5. $(y - 10)^2$
$y^2 - 20y + 100$

6. $(3x + 2)^2$
$9x^2 + 12x + 4$

7. $(4x - 3)^2$
$16x^2 - 24x + 9$

8. $(2a + 5)^2$
$4a^2 + 20a + 25$

9. $(6x + 1)^2$
$36x^2 + 12x + 1$

10. $(5b + 2)^2$
$25b^2 + 20b + 4$

11. $(4x - y)^2$
$16x^2 - 8xy + y^2$

12. $(6x - 5y)^2$
$36x^2 - 60xy + 25y^2$

13. $(3y - 5z)^2$
$9y^2 - 30yz + 25z^2$

14. $(7a + 2b)^2$
$49a^2 + 28ab + 4b^2$

15. $(11x - 2y)^2$
$121x^2 - 44xy + 4y^2$

16. $(5a + 3b)^2$
$25a^2 + 30ab + 9b^2$

Page 30

Polynomial Equations

$$
\begin{aligned}
2(2x - 1) + 5x &= 3(x - 2) + 10 \\
4x - 2 + 5x &= 3x - 6 + 10 \\
9x - 2 &= 3x + 4 \\
6x - 2 &= 4 \\
6x &= 6 \\
x &= 1
\end{aligned}
$$

1. $5(x + 2) - 4(x - 1) = 24$ $x = 10$

2. $2(y - 5) - (y + 6) = -4$ $y = 12$

3. $2(3n - 1) - (n + 6) = 7$ $n = 3$

4. $2(2b + 7) + 2(1 - 2b) = 20$ $b = \frac{1}{2}$

5. $(4x - 1) - (2x + 2) = x + 5$ $x = 8$

6. $2(y + 1) + 3(y - 1) = 9$ $y = 2$

7. $(x + 1)(x + 5) = (x + 2)(x + 3)$ $x = 1$

8. $-4r + 3(1 - 2r) = 3(5 - 2r)$ $r = -3$

9. $(y + 12)(y - 3) = y(y + 5) + 24$ $y = 15$

10. $(2x - 3)(2x - 1) = (x - 2)(4x + 3)$ $x = 3$

11. $(x - x^2) - (2x^2 + x - 1) = 5 + 2x - 3x^2$ $x = -2$

12. $t(t - 2) + 2(2t - 1) = t^2 + 4$ $t = 3$

13. $(w + 4)(w + 14) - w(w + 10) = 216$ $w = 20$

14. $(2x + 1)^2 - (2x - 1)^2 = (x + 6)^2 - x^2$ $x = -9$

Page 31

Solving Problems with Polynomials

Geometry

Find the perimeter of each polygon.

1.

$4y^2 + 4y - 14$

2.

$3x^2 - 9x + 21$

3.
$14x^2 - 12$

4.

$13y^2 - 2$

Find the area of each polygon.

5. $A = \frac{1}{2} b \cdot h$
$\frac{1}{2} \cdot 4x^2 - x - 12$

6. $A = s^2$
$4x^2 - 12x + 19$

7. $A = l \cdot w$
$21x^2 - 27x$

8. $A = s^2$

$49x^2 - 70x + 25$

Page 32

Answer Key

...More Solving Problems with Polynomials

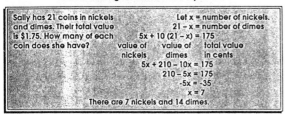

Sally has 21 coins in nickels and dimes. Their total value is $1.75. How many of each coin does she have?

Let x = number of nickels.
$21 - x$ = number of dimes.
$5x + 10 (21 - x) = 175$

value of nickels	value of dimes	total value in cents

$5x + 210 - 10x = 175$
$210 - 5x = 175$
$-5x = -35$
$x = 7$

There are 7 nickels and 14 dimes.

1. Tim bought some 25¢ and some 29¢ stamps. He paid $7.60 for 28 stamps. How many of each type of stamp did he buy?

   13 of 25¢ and 15 of 29¢

2. Tickets for the school concert were $3 and $2. If 245 tickets were sold for a total of $630, how many of each kind were sold?

   140 of $3 and 105 of $2

3. David has 11 coins, some quarters and some dimes. If the coins have a value of $1.55, how many of each kind are there?

   3 quarters and 8 dimes

4. Subtract $6x^2 - 3xy + y^2$ from $8x^2 + 5xy - y^2$.

   $2x^2 + 8xy - 2y^2$

5. From $6ab - 2ac + 5bc$, take $10ab - 2bc + 3ac$.

   $-4ab - 5ac + 7bc$

6. Subtract $x^2 - y^2 - z^2$ from the sum of $3x^2 + 2y^2 + z^2$ and $4x^2 + 3y^2 - 5z^2$.

   $6x^2 + 6y^2 - 3z^2$

7. Find the perimeter of a rectangle if its length is $(4c + 7)$ units and its width is $(c - 3)$ units.

   $P = 10c + 8$ units

8. Which has the greater area, a square with sides each $(x + 2)$ units long or a rectangle with length $(x + 4)$ units and width x units?

   square

Logic of the Obvious
(Just How Smart Are You?)

We often make mistakes by missing the obvious. Here are some examples. These are not exactly tricky questions. They are rather examples in which the obvious has been overlooked. Our habits and practices lead us to do this often.

1. If it takes 5 minutes to make one cut across a log, how long will it take to cut a 5-foot log into 5 equal pieces? **20 min.**

2. How can two fathers and two sons divide three automobiles among themselves with each receiving one? **grandfather, father, son**

3. Some months have 30 days, some have 31. How many have 28 days? **all months**

4. If a doctor gave you three pills and told you to take one every half hour, how long would they last? **1 hour**

5. I have two U.S. coins in my hand which total fifty-five cents. One is not a nickel. What are the coins? **half dollar, nickel**

6. Two men are playing chess. They played five games and each man won the same number of games with no ties. How is this possible? **They didn't play each other.**

7. Why can't a man living in St. Louis be buried in Illinois? **Because he is still living**

8. If dirt weighs 100 lb. per cubic foot, what is the weight of dirt in a hole three feet square by two feet deep? **nothing (no dirt in a hole)**

9. If you had only one match and entered a dark room in which there was a kerosene lamp, an oil burner and a wood burning stove, which would you light first? **the match**

10. Is there a fourth of July in England? **yes**

 Keep in mind...
No one is perfect...that's why pencils have erasers.

I. Greatest Common Factor (GCF)

Find the GCF of the numbers.

18, 30
$18 = 2 \cdot 3 \cdot 3$
$30 = 2 \cdot 3 \cdot 5$
$2 \cdot 3 = 6$
$6 = GCF$

1. 12, 18   **6**
2. 10, 35   **5**
3. 8, 30   **2**
4. 16, 24   **8**

5. 28, 49   **7**
6. 27, 63   **9**
7. 30, 45   **15**
8. 48, 72   **24**

II. Greatest Common Monomial Factor

Factor, write prime if prime.

$12a^2b + 15ab^2 = 3ab (4a^2 + 5b^2)$

1. $6x + 3$ **$3(2x + 1)$**
2. $24x^2 - 8x$ **$8x(3x - 1)$**
3. $6x - 12$ **$6(x - 2)$**
4. $2x^2 + 8x$ **$2x(x + 4)$**
5. $4x + 10$ **$2(2x + 5)$**
6. $10x^2 + 35x$ **$5x(2x + 7)$**
7. $10x^2y - 15xy^2$ **$5xy(2x - 3y)$**

8. $12x^2 - 9x + 15$ **$3(4x^2 - 3x + 5)$**
9. $3n^3 - 12n^2 - 30n$ **$3n(n^2 - 4n - 10)$**
10. $9m^2 - 4n + 12$ **prime**
11. $2x^3 - 3x^2 + 5x$ **$x(2x^2 - 3x + 5)$**
12. $13m + 26m^2 - 39m^3$ **$13m(1 + 2m - 3m^2)$**
13. $17x^2 + 34x + 51$ **$17(x^2 + 2x + 3)$**
14. $18m^2n^4 - 12m^2n^3 + 24m^2n^2$ **$6m^2n^2(3n^2 - 2n + 4)$**

Factoring the Difference of Two Squares

$a^2 - 36 = (a + 6)(a - 6)$
$3x^2 - 48 = 3(x^2 - 16) = 3(x + 4)(x - 4)$

Factor, write prime if prime.

1. $x^2 - 1$ **$(x + 1)(x - 1)$**
2. $x^2 - 9$ **$(x + 3)(x - 3)$**
3. $x^2 + 4$ **prime**
4. $x^2 - 25$ **$(x + 5)(x - 5)$**
5. $9y^2 - 16$ **$(3y + 4)(3y - 4)$**
6. $4x^2 - 25$ **$(2x + 5)(2x - 5)$**
7. $9x^2 - 1$ **$(3x + 1)(3x - 1)$**
8. $a^2 - x^2$ **$(a + x)(a - x)$**
9. $25 - m^2$ **$(5 + m)(5 - m)$**
10. $x^2 - 16y^2$ **$(x + 4y)(x - 4y)$**
11. $25m^2 - n^2$ **$(5m + n)(5m - n)$**

12. $-x^2 + 16$ **$(4 + x)(4 - x)$**
13. $36m^2 - 121$ **$(6m + 11)(6m - 11)$**
14. $2x^2 - 8$ **$2(x + 2)(x - 2)$**
15. $25 + 4x^2$ **prime**
16. $4a^2 - 81b^2$ **$(2a + 9b)(2a - 9b)$**
17. $12x^2 - 75$ **$3(2x + 5)(2x - 5)$**
18. $a^2b - b^3$ **$b(a + b)(a - b)$**
19. $-98 + 2x^2$ **$2(x + 7)(x - 7)$**
20. $5x^2 - 45y^2$ **$5(x + 3y)(x - 3y)$**
21. $9x^4 - 4$ **$(3x^2 + 2)(3x^2 - 2)$**
22. $16x^4 - y^2$ **$(4x^2 + y)(4x^2 - y)$**

Answer Key

Page 37

Factoring

Factoring Perfect Square Trinomials

$$x^2 - 14x + 49 = (x - 7)^2$$

Factor, write prime if prime.

1. $x^2 + 8x + 16$
$(x+4)^2$

2. $x^2 - 16x + 64$
$(x-8)^2$

3. $y^2 + 12y + 36$
$(y+6)^2$

4. $a^2 - 10a + 25$
$(a-5)^2$

5. $16y^2 + 8y + 1$
$(4y+1)^2$

6. $9x^2 - 6x + 1$
$(3x-1)^2$

7. $25x^2 + 10x + 1$
$(5x+1)^2$

8. $n^2 - 14n + 49$
$(n-7)^2$

9. $81x^2 - 90x + 25$
$(9x-5)^2$

10. $4y^2 - 20y + 25$
$(2y-5)^2$

11. $25a^2 + 60a + 36$
$(5a+6)^2$

12. $16 + 40x + 25x^2$
$(4+5x)^2$

13. $16x^2 + 24x + 9$
$(4x+3)^2$

14. $49x^2 - 14x + 1$
$(7x-1)^2$

15. $9y^2 - 30y + 25$
$(3y-5)^2$

16. $n^2 + 2n + 4$
prime

17. $b^2 + 2b + 1$
$(b+1)^2$

18. $36x^2 + 84x + 49$
$(6x+7)^2$

19. $81 - 18x + x^2$
$(x-9)^2$

20. $4 - 12y + 9y^2$
$(3y-2)^2$

Page 38

Factoring

Special Factoring—Challenge

Factor, write prime if prime.

1. $a^2 - 36$
$(a+6)(a-6)$

2. $9x^2 - 49$
$(3x+7)(3x-7)$

3. $169m^2 - 4u^2$
$(13m+2u)(13m-2u)$

4. $x^2y^2 - 9z^4$
$(xy+3z^2)(xy-3z^2)$

5. $\frac{1}{4}x^2 - 25y^2$
$(\frac{1}{2}x+5y)(\frac{1}{2}x-5y)$

6. $\frac{1}{9}x^2 - 16$
$(\frac{1}{3}x+4)(\frac{1}{3}x-4)$

7. $64 - a^4b^4$
$(8+a^2b^2)(8-a^2b^2)$

8. $y^6 - 100$
$(y^3+10)(y^3-10)$

9. $\frac{4}{9}x^2y^2 - \frac{25}{36}z^2$
$(\frac{2}{3}xy + \frac{5}{6}z)(\frac{2}{3}xy - \frac{5}{6}z)$

10. $y^8 - 81$
$(y^4+9)(y^2+3)(y^2-3)$

11. $1 - 8u + 16u^2$
$(4u-1)^2$

12. $a^2b^2 + 6ab + 9$
$(ab+3)^2$

13. $x^2 + 2xy + y^2$
$(x+y)^2$

14. $4x^2 + 12xy + 9y^2$
$(2x+3y)^2$

15. $100h^2 + 20h + 1$
$(10h+1)^2$

16. $9a^2 - 24a + 16$
$(3a-4)^2$

17. $4a^3 + 8a^2 + 4a$
$4a(a+1)^2$

18. $5c + 20c^2 + 20c^3$
$5c(2c+1)^2$

19. $(x + 4)^2 - (y + 1)^2$
$[(x+4)+(y+1)][(x+4)-(y+1)]$

20. $(x - 1)^2 - 10(x - 1) + 25$
$[(x-1)-5]^2$ or $(x-6)^2$

Page 39

Factoring

Factoring Trinomials: $x^2 + bx + c$

$$x^2 + 7x + 10 = (x)^2 + (2 + 5)x + (2)(5) = (x + 2)(x + 5)$$

Factor, write prime if prime.

1. $x^2 + 6x + 8$
$(x+4)(x+2)$

2. $c^2 + 5c + 6$
$(c+2)(c+3)$

3. $y^2 - 9y + 14$
$(y-7)(y-2)$

4. $x^2 - 10x + 16$
$(x-8)(x-2)$

5. $a^2 + 12a + 27$
$(a+9)(a+3)$

6. $x^2 - 14x + 24$
$(x-12)(x-2)$

7. $x^2 - 15x + 36$
$(x-12)(x-3)$

8. $y^2 + 21y + 54$
$(y+18)(y+3)$

9. $m^2 + 13m - 36$
Prime

10. $x^2 - 8x + 15$
$(x-5)(x-3)$

11. $y^2 - 4y - 32$
$(y-8)(y+4)$

12. $x^2 - x - 6$
$(x-3)(x+2)$

13. $y^2 + 3y - 18$
$(y+6)(y-3)$

14. $b^2 + 7b - 18$
$(b+9)(b-2)$

15. $a^2 + a - 56$
$(a+8)(a-7)$

16. $c^2 - 4c - 12$
$(c-6)(c+2)$

17. $x^2 - 9x - 36$
$(x-12)(x+3)$

18. $y^2 + 4y - 21$
$(y+7)(y-3)$

19. $x^2 - 22x - 75$
$(x-25)(x+3)$

20. $x^2 - 3x - 40$
$(x-8)(x+5)$

21. $45 + 14y + y^2$
$(y+9)(y+5)$

22. $x^2 - 13x + 36$
$(x-9)(x-4)$

Page 40

Factoring

...More Factoring Trinomials: $x^2 + bx + c$

$$k^2 - k - 20 = (k)^2 + (4 + -5)k + (4)(-5) = (k + 4)(k - 5)$$

Factor, write prime if prime.

1. $x^2 + 7x + 12$
$(x+4)(x+3)$

2. $m^2 + 10m + 21$
$(m+3)(m+7)$

3. $y^2 - 7y - 8$
$(y-8)(y+1)$

4. $x^2 - 6x + 5$
$(x-1)(x-5)$

5. $x^2 + 4x - 32$
$(x+8)(x-4)$

6. $x^2 - 2x - 15$
$(x-5)(x+3)$

7. $x^2 - 6x + 8$
$(x-2)(x-4)$

8. $y^2 + 9y + 18$
$(y+3)(y+6)$

9. $3 - 4t + t^2$
$(t-1)(t-3)$

10. $v^2 + 12v + 20$
$(v+2)(v+10)$

11. $51 - 20k + k^2$
$(k-3)(k-17)$

12. $a^2 - 14ab + 24b^2$
$(a-2b)(a-12b)$

13. $y^2 + 6y - 72$
$(y-6)(y+12)$

14. $x^2 - 11xy - 60y^2$
$(x-15y)(x+4y)$

15. $15r^2 + 2rs - s^2$
$(5r-s)(3r+s)$

16. $3x^2 + 21xy - 54y^2$
(Hint: Check for GCF)
$3(x-2y)(x+9y)$

17. $x^2 - 5xy - 6y^2$
$(x-6y)(x+1y)$

18. $x^2 + 8xy + 12y^2$
$(x+6y)(x+2y)$

19. $y^2 - 7xy + 10x^2$
$(y-5x)(y-2x)$

20. $a^2 - 11ab - 60b^2$
$(a-15b)(a+4b)$

Answer Key

Factoring Trinomials: $ax^2 + bx + c$

$$2x^2 - 5x - 3 = (2x + 1)(x - 3)$$

Factor, write prime if prime.

1. $2x^2 - 5x - 3$
$(2x+1)(x-3)$

2. $3x^2 + 10x - 8$
$(3x-2)(x+4)$

3. $2y^2 + 15y + 7$
$(2y+1)(y+7)$

4. $7a^2 - 11a + 4$
$(7a-4)(a-1)$

5. $5n^2 + 17n + 6$
$(5n+2)(n+3)$

6. $4y^2 + 8y + 3$
$(2y+3)(2y+1)$

7. $3x^2 + 4x - 7$
$(3x+7)(x-1)$

8. $2x^2 + 13x + 15$
$(2x+3)(x+5)$

9. $9y^2 + 6y - 8$
$(3y-2)(3y+4)$

10. $6x^2 - 7x - 20$
$(3x+4)(2x-5)$

11. $2n^2 - 3n - 14$
$(2n-7)(n+2)$

12. $5n^2 + 2n + 7$
prime

13. $10x^2 + 13x - 30$
$(2x+5)(5x-6)$

14. $12y^2 + 7y + 1$
$(3y+1)(4y+1)$

15. $2n^2 + 9n - 5$
$(2n-1)(n+5)$

16. $2x^2 + 7x + 6$
$(2x+3)(x+2)$

17. $5a^2 - 42a - 27$
$(5a+3)(a-9)$

18. $15x^2 - 28x - 32$
$(3x-8)(5x+4)$

19. $8a^2 - 10a + 3$
$(2a-1)(4a-3)$

20. $2y^2 - 3y - 20$
$(2y+5)(y-4)$

Page 41

Factoring

...More Factoring Trinomials: $ax^2 + bx + c$

Factor, write prime if prime.

1. $3x^2 + 4x + 1$
$(3x+1)(x+1)$

2. $5z^2 + 7z + 2$
$(5z+2)(z+1)$

3. $2n^2 - 11n + 5$
$(2n-1)(n-5)$

4. $3z^2 + z - 2$
$(3z-2)(z+1)$

5. $5h^2 - 2h - 7$
$(5h-7)(h+1)$

6. $8s^2 - 10st + 3t^2$
$(4s-3t)(2s-t)$

7. $6x^2 + 19x + 15$
$(2x+3)(3x+5)$

8. $28a^2 + 5ab - 12b^2$
$(7a-4b)(4a+3b)$

9. $2a^2 + 7ab - 15b^2$
$(2a-3b)(a+5b)$

10. $12x^2 + 17x + 6$
$(3x+2)(4x+3)$

11. $4a^2 - 4ab - 5b^2$
prime

12. $56y^2 + 15y - 56$
$(7y+8)(8y-7)$

13. $12x^2 - 29xy + 14y^2$
$(4x-7y)(3x-2y)$

14. $64x^2 + 32y - 21y^2$
$(8x+7y)(8x-3y)$

15. $16x^2 + 56xy + 49y^2$
$(4x+7y)(4x+7y)$

16. $18x^2 - 57x + 35$
$(6x-5)(3x-7)$

Page 42

Factoring

Factoring: Putting It All Together

$$5x^2 + 20x - 60 = 5(x^2 + 4x - 12) = 5(x + 6)(x - 2)$$

Factor completely, write prime if prime.

1. $2x^2 - 8$
$2(x+2)(x-2)$

2. $2x^2 + 8x + 6$
$2(x+3)(x+1)$

3. $3n^2 + 9n - 30$
$3(n+5)(n-2)$

4. $6x^2 - 26x - 20$
$2(3x+2)(x-5)$

5. $2x^2 + 12x - 80$
$2(x+10)(x-4)$

6. $5t^2 + 15t + 10$
$5(t+1)(t+2)$

7. $8n^2 - 18$
$2(2n+3)(2n-3)$

8. $14x^2 + 7x - 21$
$7(2x+3)(x-1)$

9. $4x^2 + 16x + 16$
$4(x+2)^2$

10. $18x + 12x^2 + 2x^3$
$2x(x+3)^2$

11. $2x - 2xy^2$
$2x(1+y)(1-y)$

12. $3t^3 - 27t$
$3t(t+3)(t-3)$

13. $24a^2 - 30a + 9$
$3(2a-1)(4a-3)$

14. $10x^2 + 15x - 10$
$5(2x-1)(x+2)$

15. $3x^2 - 42x + 147$
$3(x-7)^2$

16. $4x^4 - 4x^2$
$(4x^2)(x+1)(x-1)$

Page 43

Factoring

...More Factoring: Putting It All Together

1. $16x^2 - 40x - 24$
$8(2x+1)(x-3)$

2. $27x^2 - 36x + 12$
$3(3x-2)^2$

3. $5x^2 - 60x - 140$
$5(x-14)(x+2)$

4. $6m^3 + 54m^2 - 6m$
$6m(m^2+9m-1)$

5. $5k^4 + 8k^3 - 4k^2$
$k^2(5k-2)(k+2)$

6. $x^2y^4 - x^6$
$x^2(y^2+x^2)(y+x)(y-x)$

7. $y^4 - 6y^2 - 16$
$(y^2-8)(y^2+2)$

8. $x^4 - 3x^2 - 4$
$(x^2+1)(x+2)(x-2)$

9. $h^2 - (a^2 - 6a + 9)$
$[h+(a-3)][h-(a-3)]$

10. $81x^4 - 16y^4$
$(9x^2+4y^2)(3x+2y)(3x-2y)$

11. $4mn^2 - 4m^2n + m^3n^2$
$mn^2(m-2)^2$

12. $(2a + 3)^2 - (a - 1)^2$
$[(2a+3)+(a-1)][(2a+3)-(a-1)]$

13. $16d^8 - 8d^4 + 1$
$(2d^2+1)^2(2d^2-1)^2$

14. $x^2(x^2 - 4) + 4x(x^2 - 4) + 4(x^2 - 4)$
$(x+2)^3(x-2)$

Page 44

Answer Key

Factoring

Solving Equations Using Factoring

1. Rewrite equation in standard form (one member equals 0).
2. Factor completely.
3. Set each factor equal to 0; then solve.
4. Check results in original equation.

$$x^2 - 7x + 12 = 0$$
$$(x - 4)(x - 3) = 0$$
$$x - 4 = 0 \text{ or } x - 3 = 0$$
$$x = 4 \qquad x = 3$$
$$x = 3, 4$$

$$v^3 = 10v - 3v^2$$
$$v^3 + 3v^2 - 10v = 0$$
$$v(v^2 + 3v - 10) = 0$$
$$v(v + 5)(v - 2) = 0$$
$$v = 0 \text{ or } v + 5 = 0 \text{ or } v - 2 = 0$$
$$v = -5 \qquad v = 2$$
$$v = -5, 0, 2$$

1. $x^2 - 5x - 6 = 0$
   $x = 2, 3$

2. $v^3 - 4v = 0$
   $v = 0, -2, 2$

3. $n^2 - 16n = 0$
   $n = 0, 16$

4. $x^2 + 9 = 10x$
   $x = 1, 9$

5. $6x^2 = 16x - 8$
   $x = \frac{2}{3}, 2$

6. $s^2 = 56s - s^3$
   $s = -8, 0, 7$

7. $3y^2 + 2y - 1 = 0$
   $y = -1, \frac{1}{3}$

8. $u^3 = 14u^2 + 32u$
   $u = -2, 0, 16$

9. $23p = 5p^2 + 24$
   $p = \frac{8}{5}, 3$

10. $x^2 - 3x - 10 = 0$
    $x = -2, 5$

11. $y^2 = 49$
    $y = -7, 7$

12. $y^2 = -7y - 10$
    $y = -5, -2$

13. $x^2 = 8x$
    $x = 0, 8$

14. $3x^2 - 2 = x^2 + 6$
    $x = -2, 2$

15. $4y^2 = -4y - 1$
    $y = -\frac{1}{2}, -\frac{1}{2}$

16. $5x^2 - 2x - 3 = 0$
    $x = -3/5, 1$

Page 45

Factoring

Problem Solving and Factoring

Set up and solve each equation.

> The sum of the squares of two consecutive, positive, even integers is 340. Find the integers.
>
> Let $x = 1^{st}$ integer $\qquad x + 2 = 2^{nd}$ integer
> $(x)^2 + (x + 2)^2 = 340 \qquad x + 14 = 0 \text{ or } x - 12 = 0$
> $x^2 + x^2 + 4x + 4 = 340 \qquad x = -14 \qquad x = 12$
> $2x^2 + 4x - 336 = 0 \qquad\qquad$ rejected
> $2(x^2 + 2x - 168) = 0$
> $2(x + 14)(x - 12) = 0 \qquad$ The integers are 12 and 14.

1. Fourteen less than the square of a number is the same as five times the number. Find the number. **7 or -2**

2. When a number is added to six times its square, the result is -12. Find the number. **$-\frac{3}{2}$ or $-\frac{4}{3}$**

3. Find two consecutive, negative integers whose product is 156. **-13, -12**

4. The sum of the squares of two consecutive integers is 41. Find the integers. **-5, -4 or 4, 5**

5. The sum of the squares of three consecutive, positive integers is equal to the sum of the squares of the next two integers. Find the five integers. **10, 11, 12, 13, 14**

6. Find two consecutive even integers whose product is 80. **8, 10**

7. Twice the square of a certain positive number is 144 more than twice the number. What is the number? **9**

8. The square of a positive number decreased by 10 is 2 more than 4 times the number. What is the number? **6**

Page 46

Factoring

...More Problem Solving and Factoring

Set up and solve each equation.

> A square field had 9cm added to its length and 3cm added to its width. Its new area is 280cm². Find the length of a side of the original field.
>
> Let x = length of a side of the square field
> $(x + 9)(x + 3) = 280$
> $x^2 + 12x + 27 = 280$
> $x^2 + 12x - 253 = 0$
> $(x + 23)(x - 11) = 0$
> $x + 23 = 0 \text{ or } x - 11 = 0$
> $x = -23 \qquad x = 11 \qquad$ The side of the square was
> rejected $\qquad\qquad\qquad$ 11 cm.

1. The length of a rectangle is 5m greater than twice its width, and its area is 33m². Find the dimensions. **3 x 11**

2. The perimeter of a rectanglular piece of property is 8 miles, and its area is 3 square miles. Find the dimensions. (Hint: $\frac{1}{2}P = l + w$) **1 x 3**

3. When the dimensions of a 2cm X 5cm rectangle were increased by equal amounts, the area was increased by 18cm². Find the dimensions of the new rectangle. **4 x 7**

4. If the sides of a square are increased by 3 in., the area becomes 64 in.² Find the length of a side of the original square. **5**

5. A rug placed in a 10 ft X 12 ft room covers two-thirds of the floor area and leaves a uniform strip of bare floor around the edges. Find the dimensions of the rug. **8 x 10**

6. The area of a rectangular pool is 192 square meters. The lengh of the pool is 4 meters more than its width. Find the length and width. **12 x 16**

Page 47

Factoring

Extra: Factoring by Grouping

> $6ax - 2b - 3a + 4bx = 6ax - 3a + 4b - 2b$
> $\qquad = 3a(2x - 1) + 2b(2x - 1)$
> $\qquad = (2x - 1)(3a + 2b)$

1. $x^2 + 2x + xy + 2y$
   $(x + 2)(x + y)$

2. $3a^2 - 2b - 6a + ab$
   $(a + 2)(3a + b)$

3. $t^3 - t^2 + \underline{t - 1}$
   Hint: $t - 1 = 1(t - 1)$
   $(t - 1)(t^2 + 1)$

4. $10 + 2t - 5s - st$
   $(2 - s)(t + 5)$

5. $\frac{2}{3}bc - \frac{14}{3}b + c - 7$
   $(c - 7)(\frac{2}{3}b + 1)$

6. $4u^2 + v + 2uv + 2u$
   $(2u + 1)(2u + v)$

7. $ad + 3a - d^2 - 3d$
   $(a - d)(d + 3)$

8. $n^2 + 2n + 3mn + 6m$
   $(n + 3m)(n + 2)$

9. $2ax^2 + bx^2 - 2ay^2 - by^2$
   $(x - y)(x + y)(2a + b)$

10. $yz^2 - y^3 + z^3 - y^2z$
    $(z - y)(z + y)^2$

11. $y^3 - y^2 - 4y + 4$
    $(y + 2)(y - 2)(y - 1)$

12. $x^2a + x^2b - 16a - 16b$
    $(x + 4)(x - 4)(a + b)$

13. $x^3 + x^2 - x - 1$
    $(x + 1)^2(x - 1)$

14. $a^3 - a^2 - 8a + 8$
    $(a - 1)(a^2 - 8)$

Page 48

Answer Key

Factoring

Logic of the Obvious

1. How far can a dog run into the woods? **Halfway, the other half it is running out.**

2. If 30 is divided by $\frac{1}{2}$ and added to 10, what is the answer? **70**

3. Rearrange the letters of NEW DOOR to make one word. **ONE WORD**

4. In a tennis tournament there are 39 entries. How many matches must be played before there is a champion? **1 match, the final**

5. A rope ladder is hanging over the side of the ship. Five rungs are below the surface of the water. During the night the tide comes in and the water rises at the rate of 16 inches an hour. How many rungs will be in the water after 3 hours? **5 rungs, the ship will float at the same level on the water**

6. How many birthdays does the average man have? **1 birth day**

7. A man builds a house with four sides to it, a rectangular structure. Each side has a southern exposure. A big bear comes wandering by. What color is the bear? **White (polar bear)**

8. How many men are on a baseball team? How many outs in each inning? **at least 9, 6**

9. Is it legal in North Carolina for a man to marry his widow's sister? **NO, if a man has a widow, he is dead.**

10. What do you have if you take 2 apples from 5 apples? **The two apples you took.**

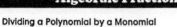 Page 49

Algebraic Fractions

☞ Keep in mind...
The dictionary is the only place where success comes before work.

Dividing Monomials

$$\frac{18x^4y}{-3x^3y^5} = \frac{18}{-3} \cdot \frac{x^{4-3}}{1} \cdot \frac{1}{y^{5-1}} = \frac{-6x^1}{y^4}$$

1. $\frac{m^{10}}{m^5}$ m^5

2. $\frac{x^3y^2}{2x^2y^2}$ $\frac{x}{2}$

3. $\frac{4ab^3}{2a^2b^2}$ $\frac{2b}{a}$

4. $\frac{27u^2v^3}{-18u^4v^5}$ $\frac{3}{-2u^2v^2}$

5. $\frac{13c^9d^{10}}{-26c^9d}$ $\frac{d^9}{-2}$

6. $\frac{3s^5t^7}{-3s^5t^7}$ -1

7. $\frac{-52x^3y^2z}{13xy^2}$ $-4x^2z$

8. $\frac{8xy^2}{16x^3y^5}$ $\frac{1}{2x^2y^3}$

9. $\frac{5x^4}{5}$ x^4

10. $\frac{18x^2y}{24xy}$ $\frac{3x}{4}$

11. $\frac{56s^2t^3}{4s^2t}$ $14t^2$

12. $\frac{48a^3bc^5}{12a^5b^3c^2}$ $\frac{4c^3}{a^2b^2}$

13. $\frac{25x^2y}{-15xy^2}$ $-\frac{5x}{3y}$

14. $\frac{8m^2n^2}{12m^2n^3}$ $\frac{2}{3n}$

15. $\frac{-17c^5d^4}{-51cd^3}$ $\frac{c^4d}{3}$

16. $\frac{24x^2y^3z^4}{-44x^4y^3z^2}$ $\frac{6z^2}{-11x^2}$

Page 50

Algebraic Fractions

Dividing a Polynomial by a Monomial

$$\frac{r^2 + 6r + 5}{r} = \frac{r^2}{r} + \frac{6r}{r} + \frac{5}{r}$$
$$= r + 6 + \frac{5}{r}$$

1. $\frac{a^2 + 2a}{a}$ $a+2$

2. $\frac{14x + 35}{7}$ $2x+5$

3. $\frac{4y^2 + 6y}{2y}$ $2y+3$

4. $\frac{x^2y - xy^2}{xy}$ $x-y$

5. $\frac{25u^2 - 15u - 5}{-5}$ $-5u^2+3u+1$

6. $\frac{12x^2 - 9x^3 + 6x^4}{3x}$ $4x-3x^2+2x^3$

7. $\frac{m^2n^2 + m - n}{mn}$ $mn+\frac{1}{n}-\frac{1}{m}$

8. $\frac{45a^2b^4 - 60a^3b^2 - 15a^2b}{-15a^2b}$ $-3b^3+4ab+1$

9. $\frac{14k^6m^3 - 4k^2m^2 + 12km^3}{2km^2}$ $7k^5m-2k+6m$

10. $\frac{12v^5 - 27v^4 + 18uv^3}{3uv^3}$ $4\frac{v^2}{u}-\frac{9v}{u}+6$

11. $\frac{2x^2 - 10xy}{2x}$ $x-5y$

12. $\frac{3x^3y^2 - 6x^2y^2 + 6xy^2}{3xy}$ $x^2y-2xy+2y$

13. $\frac{6z^2 - 3z + 9}{3z}$ $2z-1+\frac{3}{z}$

14. $\frac{6a^2 + 42a + 72}{6a^3}$ $\frac{1}{a}+\frac{7}{a^2}+\frac{12}{a^3}$

15. $\frac{64x^4 - 64x^3}{64x^3}$ $x-1$

16. $\frac{18m^3n^4 - 12m^2n^3 + 24n^2}{6m^2n}$ $3mn^3-2n^2+\frac{4n}{m^2}$

Page 51

Algebraic Fractions

Simplifying Fractions

$$\frac{5x^2 + 30x - 35}{5 - 5x^2} = \frac{5(x+7)(x-1)}{-5(x+1)(x-1)}$$
$$= \frac{x+7}{x+1}$$

1. $\frac{8a - 8b}{a^2 - b^2}$ $\frac{8}{a+b}$

2. $\frac{x^2 + 8x + 16}{x^2 - 16}$ $\frac{x+4}{x-4}$

3. $\frac{12 - 4a}{a^2 + a - 12}$ $\frac{-4}{a+4}$

4. $\frac{t^2 + 4t - 5}{t^2 + 9t + 20}$ $\frac{t-1}{t+4}$

5. $\frac{z^2 - 4z - 5}{z^2 + 4z - 45}$ $\frac{z+1}{z+9}$

6. $\frac{6b^3 - 24b^2}{b^2 + b - 20}$ $\frac{6b^2}{b^2+5}$

7. $\frac{-x^2 + 8x - 12}{x - 2}$ $6-x$

8. $\frac{2a^3 + a^2 - 3a}{6a^3 + 5a^2 - 6a}$ $\frac{a-1}{3a-2}$

9. $\frac{x^2 - 9}{x^2 + x - 6}$ $\frac{x-3}{x-2}$

10. $\frac{3x^2 + 2x - 1}{x^2 + 3x + 2}$ $\frac{3x-1}{x+2}$

11. $\frac{x^2 + 5x}{x^2 - 25}$ $\frac{x}{x-5}$

12. $\frac{a^2 - 11a + 30}{a^2 - 9a + 18}$ $\frac{a-5}{a-3}$

13. $\frac{2y^3 - 12y^2 + 2y}{y^2 - 6y + 1}$ $2y$

14. $\frac{a + b}{a^2 + 2ab + b^2}$ $\frac{1}{a+b}$

Page 52

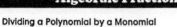

Answer Key

Algebraic Fractions

Multiplying Fractions

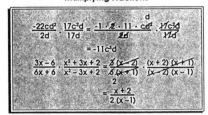

1. $\frac{24r^2s^2}{3s} \cdot \frac{-21s}{r}$ $-168rs^2$

2. $\frac{x^2y}{z^2} \cdot \frac{z}{xy}$ $\frac{x}{z}$

3. $\frac{2t+16}{4t} \cdot \frac{10t^2}{3t+24}$ $\frac{5}{3}t$

4. $\frac{x^2-1}{x} \cdot \frac{x^2}{x-1}$ x^2+x

5. $\frac{a+b}{a-b} \cdot \frac{a^2-b^2}{a+b}$ $a+b$

6. $\frac{a^2-4}{a^2-1} \cdot \frac{a-1}{a-1}$ $\frac{(a-2)(a+2)}{(a-1)(a+1)}$

7. $\frac{2x+2}{x-1} \cdot \frac{x^2+x-2}{x^2-x-2}$ $\frac{2(x+2)}{x-2}$

8. $\frac{z^2-6z-7}{z^2+z} \cdot \frac{z^2-z}{3z-21}$ $\frac{z-1}{3}$

9. $\frac{c^2-6c-16}{c^2+4c-21} \cdot \frac{c^2-8c+15}{c^2+9c+14}$ $\frac{(c-8)(c-5)}{(c+7)^2}$

10. $\frac{x+8}{x^2-x-12} \cdot \frac{x^2-6x+8}{x^2+6x-16}$ $\frac{1}{x+3}$

11. $\frac{h^2-2h-3}{h^2-9} \cdot \frac{h^2+5h+6}{h^2-1}$ $\frac{h+2}{h-1}$

12. $\frac{x^2-y^2}{x^2+4xy+3y^2} \cdot \frac{x^2+xy-6y^2}{x^2+xy-2y^2}$ $\frac{x-2y}{x+2y}$

13. $\frac{30+y-y^2}{25-y^2} \cdot \frac{y^2}{y^2-6y} \cdot \frac{y^2-y-12}{y^2-9}$ $\frac{y(4-y)}{(5-y)(y-3)}$

14. $\frac{5m+5n}{m^2-n^2} \cdot \frac{m^2-mn}{(m+n)^2}$ $\frac{5m}{(m+n)^2}$

Algebraic Fractions

Dividing Fractions

$$\frac{12a^2b^2}{21xy^2} \div \frac{4ab^2}{7y^2} = \frac{12a^2b^2}{21xy^2} \cdot \frac{7y^2}{4ab^2}$$
$$= \frac{a}{x}$$

1. $\frac{b+2}{b^2-9} \div \frac{1}{b-3}$ $\frac{b+2}{b+3}$

2. $\frac{c^2+2cd}{2cd+d^2} \div \frac{c^3+2c^2d}{cd+d^2}$ $\frac{c+d}{c(2c+d)}$

3. $\frac{x^2+3x^3}{4-x^2} \div \frac{x+4x^2+3x^3}{2x+x^2}$ $\frac{x^2(x+3)}{(2-x)(3x+1)(x+1)}$

4. $\frac{a^2-a-20}{a^2+7a+12} \div \frac{a^2-7a+10}{a^2+9a+18}$ $\frac{a+6}{a-2}$

5. $\frac{6a^2-a-2}{12a^2+5a-2} \div \frac{4a^2-1}{8a^2-6a+1}$ $\frac{3a-2}{3a+2}$

6. $\frac{a^3-6a^2+8a}{5a} \div \frac{2a-4}{10a-40}$ $(a-4)^2$

7. $\frac{12x+36}{x^2-2x-8} \div \frac{15x+45}{x^2+x-20}$ $\frac{4(x+5)}{5(x+2)}$

8. $\frac{x^2-y^2}{x^2+2xy+y^2} \div \frac{x-y}{x+y}$ 1

9. $(y^2-9) \div \frac{y^2+8y+15}{2y+10}$ $2(y-3)$

10. $\frac{x^2-4x+4}{3x-6} \div (x-2)$ $\frac{1}{3}$

11. $\frac{(2a)^3}{(4bc)^3} \div \frac{16a^2}{8b^2c^3}$ $\frac{a}{16b}$

12. $\frac{\frac{26c^2}{5c^2d}}{\frac{13c^3}{25d^3}}$ $\frac{10d^2}{c^3}$

Algebraic Fractions

Combination Problems

Express answers in simplest form.

1. $\frac{6x}{3x-7} \cdot \frac{9x-21}{21} \div \frac{x^2}{35}$ $\frac{30}{x}$

2. $\frac{x^2-x-6}{x^2+2x-15} \cdot \frac{x^2-25}{x^2-4x-5} \div \frac{x^2+5x+6}{x^2-1}$ $\frac{x-1}{x+3}$

3. $\frac{x-y}{x+y} \div \frac{5x^2-5y^2}{3x-3y} \cdot \frac{(x+y)^2}{x^2-y^2}$ $\frac{3}{5(x+y)}$

4. $(b^2-9) \div \frac{b^2+8b+15}{2b+10} \div (b-3)$ 2

5. $\frac{a^3b^3}{a^3-ab^2} \div \frac{abc}{a-b} \cdot \frac{ab+bc}{ab}$ $\frac{b^2(a+c)}{c(a+b)}$

6. $\frac{x^2+16x+64}{x^2-9} \div \frac{x^2-64}{x+3} \cdot x^2-11x+24$ $x+8$

Algebraic Fractions

Adding and Subtracting Fractions with Like Denominators

$$\frac{5}{17} + \frac{3}{17} - \frac{11}{17} = \frac{5+3-11}{17}$$
$$= \frac{-3}{17}$$

$$\frac{5a+3c}{2a} - \frac{a-c}{2a} = \frac{5a+3c-(a-c)}{2a}$$
$$= \frac{5a+3c-a+c}{2a}$$
$$= \frac{4a+4c}{2a}$$
$$= \frac{2 \cdot 2(a+c)}{2a}$$
$$= \frac{2(a+c)}{a}$$

1. $\frac{2}{x} - \frac{8}{x} + \frac{3}{x}$ $-\frac{3}{x}$

2. $\frac{3a}{5b} + \frac{2a}{5b}$ $\frac{a}{b}$

3. $\frac{r}{6} - \frac{5t}{6}$ $\frac{r-5t}{6}$

4. $\frac{x+y}{2} - \frac{x}{2}$ $\frac{y}{2}$

5. $\frac{c}{c-d} - \frac{d}{c-d}$ 1

6. $\frac{6a}{a+d} + \frac{6d}{a+d}$ 6

7. $\frac{x^2}{x-2} - \frac{4}{x-2}$ $x+2$

8. $\frac{c^2}{c^2-4} - \frac{6c+16}{c^2-4}$ $\frac{c-8}{c-2}$

9. $\frac{x^2-7x}{(x-3)^2} + \frac{12}{(x-3)^2}$ $\frac{x-4}{x-3}$

10. $\frac{x^2}{2x+14} - \frac{49}{2x+14}$ $\frac{x-7}{2}$

11. $\frac{7x}{2y+5} - \frac{6x}{2y+5}$ $\frac{x}{2y+5}$

12. $\frac{y+4}{y-5} - \frac{3y+1}{y-5}$ $\frac{-2y+3}{y-5}$

13. $\frac{2x-3}{2} - \frac{6x-5}{2}$ $-2x+1$

14. $\frac{8a-1}{5} - \frac{3a-6}{5}$ $a+1$

Answer Key

Adding and Subtracting Fractions with Unlike Denominators

$$\frac{1}{7} - \frac{a}{b} = \frac{1 \cdot b}{7 \cdot b} - \frac{7 \cdot a}{7 \cdot b}$$
$$= \frac{b}{7b} - \frac{7a}{7b}$$
$$= \frac{b - 7a}{7b}$$

$$\frac{3}{x^2} + \frac{5}{2xy} - \frac{4}{3y^2} = \frac{3 \cdot 6y^2}{x^2 \cdot 6y^2} + \frac{5 \cdot 3xy}{2xy \cdot 3xy} - \frac{4 \cdot 2x^2}{3y^2 \cdot 2x^2}$$
$$= \frac{18y^2 + 15xy - 8x^2}{6x^2y^2}$$

1. $\frac{1}{x} + \frac{1}{y}$ $\frac{y+x}{xy}$ or $\frac{x+y}{xy}$

2. $\frac{3n}{7} + \frac{n}{14}$ $\frac{n}{2}$

3. $\frac{2x}{3} + \frac{5y}{2}$ $\frac{4x+15y}{6}$

4. $\frac{x}{3} + \frac{x^2}{5}$ $\frac{3x^2+5x}{15}$

5. $\frac{2x}{x^2y} - \frac{y}{xy^2}$ $\frac{1}{xy}$

6. $\frac{5}{12xy} + \frac{3}{4x}$ $\frac{9y+5}{12xy}$

7. $\frac{a}{b} - \frac{c}{d}$ $\frac{ad-bc}{bd}$

8. $\frac{8}{x} + \frac{3}{xy}$ $\frac{8y+3}{xy}$

9. $\frac{4x-1}{3x} + \frac{x-8}{5x}$ $\frac{23x-29}{15x}$

10. $\frac{2x+1}{4} - \frac{x-1}{8}$ $\frac{3x+3}{8}$ or $\frac{3(x+1)}{8}$

11. $\frac{a+2b}{3} + \frac{a+b}{2}$ $\frac{5a+7b}{6}$

12. $\frac{1}{x} + \frac{2}{x^2} - \frac{3}{x^3}$ $\frac{x^2+2x-3}{(x+3)(x-1)}$ or $\frac{x^2+2x-3}{x^3}$

...More Adding and Subtracting Fractions with Unlike Denominators

$$\frac{x+1}{x^2-9} + \frac{4}{x+3} - \frac{x-1}{x-3} = \frac{x+1}{(x+3)(x-3)} + \frac{4(x-3)}{(x+3)(x-3)} - \frac{(x-1)(x+3)}{(x-3)(x+3)}$$
$$= \frac{x+1+4x-12-(x^2+2x-3)}{(x+3)(x-3)}$$
$$= \frac{5x-11-x^2-2x+3}{(x+3)(x-3)}$$
$$= \frac{-x^2+3x-8}{x^2-9}$$

1. $\frac{3a+2b}{3b} - \frac{a+2b}{6a}$ $\frac{6a^2+3ab-2b^2}{6ab}$

2. $\frac{a}{2a+2b} - \frac{b}{3a+3b}$ $\frac{3a-2b}{6(a+b)}$

3. $\frac{3x}{2y-3} + \frac{2x}{3-2y}$ $\frac{x}{2y-3}$ Hint: $3-2y = -1(2y-3)$

4. $\frac{x}{x+3} + \frac{9x+18}{x^2+3x}$ $\frac{x+6}{x}$

5. $\frac{x+3}{x-5} + \frac{x-5}{x+3}$ $\frac{2(17-2x)}{(x-5)(x+3)}$

6. $\frac{11x}{x^2+3x-28} + \frac{x}{x+7}$ $\frac{x}{x-4}$

7. $\frac{d^2+3}{d^2-2d} - \frac{d-4}{d}$ $\frac{6d-5}{d(d-2)}$

8. $\frac{4a}{2a+6} - \frac{a-1}{a+3}$ $\frac{a+1}{a+3}$

9. $\frac{a+b}{ax+ay} - \frac{a+b}{bx+by}$ $\frac{(b+a)(b-a)}{ab(x+y)}$

10. $\frac{8}{c^2-4} + \frac{2}{c^2-5c+6}$ $\frac{10}{(c-3)(c+2)}$

11. $\frac{x}{x^2-16} + \frac{6}{4-x} - \frac{1}{x-4}$ $\frac{2(3x+14)}{(4-x)(x+4)}$

12. $\frac{1}{a^2-a-2} + \frac{1}{a^2+2a+1}$ $\frac{2a-1}{(a-2)(a+1)^2}$

13. $\frac{5}{3x-3} + \frac{x}{2x+2} - \frac{3x^2}{x^2-1}$ $\frac{-15x^2+7x+10}{6(x+1)(x-1)}$

14. $\frac{x+1}{x^2-9} + \frac{4}{x+3} - \frac{x-1}{x-3}$ $\frac{-x^2+3x-8}{(x+3)(x-3)}$

Simplifying Mixed Expressions

$$\frac{a}{x+3} + \frac{a}{x-3} - 2 = \frac{a(x-3)}{(x+3)(x-3)} + \frac{a(x+3)}{(x+3)(x-3)} - \frac{2(x+3)(x-3)}{(x+3)(x-3)}$$
$$= \frac{ax-3a+ax+3a-2x^2+18}{(x+3)(x-3)}$$
$$= \frac{2ax-2x^2+18}{x^2-9}$$

1. $b + \frac{6}{b-1}$ $\frac{(b-3)(b+2)}{b-1}$

2. $3 + \frac{a+2b}{a-b}$ $\frac{4a-b}{a-b}$

3. $x - y + \frac{1}{x+y}$ $\frac{x^2-y^2+1}{x+y}$

4. $7 + \frac{3}{a} + \frac{6}{b}$ $\frac{7ab+3b+6a}{ab}$

5. $\frac{5}{x+2} + 1$ $\frac{x+7}{x+2}$

6. $d + 3 + \frac{2d-1}{d-2}$ $\frac{d^2+3d-7}{d-2}$

7. $\frac{2x-3}{x+2} - 4$ $\frac{-2x-11}{x+2}$

8. $2x - \frac{x+y}{y}$ $\frac{2xy-x-y}{y}$

9. $\frac{8}{3a-1} - 6$ $\frac{14-18a}{3a-1}$

10. $(x-4) - \frac{1}{x-2}$ $\frac{x^2-6x+7}{x-2}$

11. $\frac{x}{2y} - (x+2)$ $\frac{x-2xy-4y}{2y}$

12. $(a+2) + \frac{7}{a-2}$ $\frac{a^2+3}{a-2}$

13. $4 - \frac{3}{y-1} - \frac{1}{y+1}$ $\frac{4y^2-4y-6}{y^2-1}$

14. $\frac{\frac{a}{b}+1}{\frac{a}{b}-1}$ $\frac{a+b}{a-b}$

Dividing Polynomials

$$\frac{6a2+4a+3}{3a-1} \Rightarrow 3a-1 \overline{\smash{\big)}6a^2+4a+3} \quad \frac{2a+2+\frac{5}{3a-1}}{}$$
$$\underline{6a^2-2a}$$
$$6a+3$$
$$\underline{6a-2}$$
$$5$$

1. $\frac{s^2+3s-4}{4+s}$ $s-1$ (Hint: Rewrite denominator as s + 4)

2. $\frac{a^2+2a+3}{a+3}$ $a-1 + \frac{6}{a+3}$

3. $\frac{x^2+4}{x+2}$ $x-2 + \frac{8}{x+2}$ (Hint: Write dividend as x² + 0x + 4)

4. $\frac{3c^2+8c+4}{3c+2}$ $c+2$

5. $\frac{6r^2+r-5}{2r-3}$ $3r+5 + \frac{10}{2r-3}$

6. $\frac{9t^2+1}{3t+2}$ $3t-2 + \frac{5}{3t+2}$

7. $\frac{2u^2-3uv-9v^2}{u-3v}$ $2u+3v$

8. $\frac{z^3+z^2-3z+9}{z+3}$ z^2-2z+3

9. $\frac{6x^3+5x^2+9}{2x+3}$ $3x^2-2x+3$

10. $\frac{2y^3+5y^2+7y+6}{y^2+y+2}$ $2y+3$

11. $x^3-x^2-2x+10 \div x+2$ $x^2-3x+4 + \frac{2}{x+2}$

12. $8x+13x^2+6x^3+5 \div 3x+5$ $2x^2+x+1$

13. $y^3-2y^2+3 \div y+1$ y^2-3y+3

14. $\frac{-32x+2x^3+42}{2x-6}$ x^2+3x-7

Algebraic Fractions
Synthetic Division

$$\frac{x^2 - 5x - 24}{x + 3} \Rightarrow -3 \begin{array}{|rrr} 1 & -5 & -24 \\ & -3 & 24 \\ \hline 1 & -8 & 0 \end{array}$$

$$= x - 8$$

1. $y^2 - 13y + 36 \div y - 4$

(Hint: 4 $\begin{array}{|rr} 1 & -13 & 36 \end{array}$)

$y - 9$

2. $x^2 + 10x + 21 \div x + 3$

$x + 7$

3. $4a^2 + 19a + 21 \div a + 1$

$4a + 15 + \frac{6}{a+1}$

4. $x^3 - 5x^2 + 2x + 8 \div x - 2$

$x^2 - 3x - 4$

5. $y^2 + 25 \div y + 5$

$y - 5 + \frac{50}{y+5}$

6. $x^3 + 2x^2 - 2x + 24 \div x + 4$

$x^2 - 2x + 6$

Algebraic Fractions
Ratios

I. Express each ratio as a fraction in simplest form.

45 seconds to 3 minutes
$$\frac{45}{3 \cdot 60} = \frac{45 \text{ sec}}{180 \text{ sec}} = \frac{1}{4}$$

The ratio of males to total students in a school with 1200 males and 1000 females.
$$\frac{1200}{1000 + 1200} = \frac{1200 \text{ males}}{2200 \text{ students}} = \frac{6}{11}$$

1. 55¢ to $4 $\frac{11}{80}$
2. 10 inches to 1 yard $\frac{5}{18}$
3. 8 hours to 3 days $\frac{1}{9}$
4. The ratio of wins to losses in 35 games with 21 losses and no ties. $\frac{2}{3}$
5. The ratio of the area of a rectangle with sides of 6m and 8m to the area of a square with sides of length 12m. $\frac{1}{3}$
6. The ratio of girls to boys in a class of 40 students with 17 girls. $\frac{17}{23}$
7. Big Bob's batting average if he had 3 hits in 4 at bats against the Cougars. $\frac{3}{4}$
8. The ratio of wins to losses in 42 games with 35 wins and no ties. $\frac{5}{1}$

II. Set up and solve each of the following.

Find two numbers in the ratio of 4:3 whose sum is 63.
Let x = common factor $4x + 3x = 63$ $4 \cdot 9 = 36$
$4x$ = first number $7x = 63$ $3 \cdot 9 = 27$
$3x$ = second number $x = 9$ The numbers are 36 and 27.

9. A 36 cm segment is divided into three parts whose lengths have the ratio of 2:3:7. Find the length of each segment. 6cm, 9cm, 21cm
10. The sum of the measures of two complementary angles is 90°. Find the measures of two complementary angles whose measures are in the ratio of 1:4. 18°, 72°

Algebraic Fractions
Proportions

$$\frac{x}{12} = \frac{5}{3}$$
$$3x = 12 \cdot 5$$
$$3x = 60$$
$$x = 20$$

A pipe delivers 5 gallons of water in 45 seconds. How much will it deliver in 15 minutes?
$$\frac{5 \text{ gal}}{45 \text{ sec}} = \frac{x \text{ gal}}{15 \cdot 60 \text{ sec}}$$
$$45x = 5 \cdot 900$$
$$45x = 4500$$
$$x = 100 \qquad 100 \text{ gallons}$$

1. $\frac{9}{11} = \frac{16}{x}$ $x = 19\frac{5}{9}$
2. $\frac{5}{13} = \frac{a}{65}$ $a = 25$
3. $\frac{y}{2.5} = \frac{21}{5}$ $y = 10.5$
4. $\frac{z-8}{21} = \frac{1}{3}$ $z = 15$
5. $\frac{2x+1}{3} = \frac{4}{5}$ $x = \frac{7}{10}$
6. $\frac{n}{16-n} = \frac{5}{3}$ $n = 10$
7. $\frac{2x+1}{9} = \frac{x}{4}$ $x = 4$
8. $\frac{3m}{m+4} = \frac{5}{3}$ $m = 5$
9. $\frac{x-2}{x} = \frac{x-1}{x+2}$ $x = 4$

10. If 30m. of wire weigh 8 kilograms, what will 40m of the same kind of wire weigh? $10\frac{2}{3}$ kg
11. On a map, $1\frac{1}{2}$ cm represents 60 km. What distance does 6 cm represent? 240 Km
12. A post casts a shadow 9 feet long. A girl 5 feet tall casts a shadow 15 feet long at the same time and place. How tall is the pole? 3 ft
13. If Marilyn drove 270 miles in $4\frac{1}{2}$ hours, how far would she travel in 7 hours? 420 miles
14. The sales tax on an $800 purchase is $24. At this rate, what is the tax on a $600 purchase? $18

Algebraic Fractions
Percents

Find 25% of $240.
$$\frac{25}{100} = \frac{x}{240}$$
$$100x = 25 \cdot 240$$
$$100x = 6000$$
$$x = \$60$$

If 20% of a number is 32, find the number.
$$\frac{20}{100} = \frac{32}{x}$$
$$20x = 32 \cdot 100$$
$$20x = 3200$$
$$x = 160$$
The number is 160.

What percent is 15 out of 45?
$$\frac{x}{100} = \frac{15}{45}$$
$$45x = 100 \cdot 15$$
$$45x = 1500$$
$$x = 33\frac{1}{3}$$
$$33\frac{1}{3}\%$$

1. 72% of 310 223.1
2. 21 is 35% of what number? 60
3. 28 out of 70 is what percent? 40%
4. .6% of what number is 2.36? $39\frac{1}{3}$
5. 3.9 is what percent of 10? 39%
6. 115% of 12 13.8
7. 60% of what number is 54? 90
8. 17% of 800 is what number? 136
9. What percent of 72 is 27? 37.5

10. A piece of jewelry costs $78. If the price increases by 12%, what is the new cost? $87.36
11. Tax on a $24 item is $1.56. What is the tax rate (percent)? 6.5%
12. A dress was reduced in price by $19.56. This was 20% of the original price. Find the sale price. $78.24
13. There are 252 students on the student council at West High School. If there are 700 students enrolled, what percent are on the student council? 36%
14. One day 3% of the sweatshirts made at a factory were defective. 15 sweatshirts were defective. How many sweatshirts were produced at the factory that day? 500

Answer Key

Algebraic Fractions
Solving Fractional Equations

$$\frac{2}{3x} + \frac{1}{2} = \frac{3}{4x}$$
$$12x \cdot \frac{2}{3x} + 12x \cdot \frac{1}{2} = 12x \cdot \frac{3}{4x}$$
$$8 + 6x = 9$$
$$6x = 1$$
$$x = \frac{1}{6}$$

1. $\frac{5}{6x} + 3 = \frac{1}{2x}$ $x = -\frac{1}{9}$

2. $\frac{2}{5n} = \frac{3}{10n} - \frac{3}{5}$ $n = -\frac{1}{6}$

3. $\frac{4}{3x} - \frac{5}{2x} = 5\frac{1}{6x}$ $x = -\frac{4}{15}$

4. $\frac{c-7}{c+2} = \frac{1}{4}$ $c = 10$

5. $\frac{y}{y-3} = 2$ $y = 6$

6. $\frac{2x}{5} + \frac{1}{2} = \frac{3x}{10}$ $x = -5$

7. $\frac{x}{x-2} = \frac{4}{5}$ $x = -8$

8. $\frac{2}{3} = \frac{y}{y+3}$ $y = 6$

9. $\frac{10}{x-3} = \frac{9}{x-5}$ $x = 23$

10. $\frac{7}{x} - \frac{4x}{2x-3} = -2$ $x = 2\frac{5}{8}$

11. $\frac{3}{x} + \frac{1}{2x} = \frac{7}{8}$ $x = 4$

12. $\frac{3}{4} = \frac{x+5}{x-2}$ $x = -26$

Page 65

Algebraic Fractions
...More Solving Fractional Equations

$$\frac{2}{x^2-x} - \frac{2}{x-1} = 1$$
$$x(x-1) \cdot \frac{2}{x(x-1)} - x(x-1)\frac{2}{x-1} = x(x-1) \cdot 1$$
$$2 - 2x = x^2 - x$$
$$0 = x^2 + x - 2$$
$$0 = (x+2)(x-1)$$
$$x+2 = 0 \quad x - 1 = 0 \text{ 1 is rejected because}$$
$$x = -2 \quad x = 1 \text{ denominator} \neq 0.$$

1. $\frac{1}{u+4} + \frac{1}{u-4} = \frac{6}{u^2-16}$ $u = 3$

2. $\frac{x}{8} + \frac{1}{x-2} = \frac{x+2}{2x-4}$ $x = 26$

3. $\frac{5y}{y+1} - \frac{y}{y+6} = 4$ $y = 24$

4. $\frac{d}{d-2} = \frac{d+3}{d+2} - \frac{d}{d^2-4}$ $d = -3$

5. $\frac{6y}{2y+1} - \frac{3}{y} = -1$ $y = -\frac{3}{8}, y = 1$

6. $2 + \frac{4}{b-1} = \frac{4}{b^2-b}$ $b = -2$

7. $\frac{2z^2+z-3}{z^2+1} = 2$ $z = 5$

8. $\frac{x}{x-3} + \frac{2}{x+4} = 1$ $x = -\frac{6}{5}$

9. $\frac{1}{m-3} + \frac{1}{m+5} = \frac{m+1}{m-3}$ $m = -1, m = -3$

10. $\frac{c}{c+1} + \frac{3}{c-3} + 1 = 0$ $c = 0, c = 1$

11. $\frac{b}{b+1} - \frac{b+1}{b-4} = \frac{5}{b^2-3b-4}$ No solution

12. $\frac{2}{2y+1} - \frac{1}{2y} = \frac{3}{2y+1}$ $y = -\frac{1}{4}$

Page 66

Algebraic Fractions
Problem Solving: Mixture Problems

How much water must be added to 20kg of a 10% salt solution to produce a 5% solution?
Let x = amount of water
$10\% \cdot 20 + 0\% x = 5\% \cdot (x + 20)$
$2 + 0 = .05x + 1$
$1 = .05x$
$20 = x$ 20 kg of water

1. How much water must be added to 60kg of an 80% acid solution to produce a 50% solution?   36 kg of water

2. How much water must be evaporated from 8 grams of a 30% antiseptic solution to produce a 40% solution?   2 grams

3. How many grams of alcohol must be added to 40 grams of a 15% alcohol solution to obtain a 20% alcohol solution?   2.5 grams

4. How many quarts of antifreeze must be added to 15 quarts of a 30% antifreeze solution to obtain a 50% antifreeze solution?   6 quarts

5. A candy mixture is created with 2 types of candy, one costing $4 per pound and the other $3.50 per pound. How much of each type is needed for a 5 pound box that costs $18?   1 pound of $4 and 4 pounds of $3.50

6. A seed company mixes two types of seed for bird feeding. One costs $1.10 per kg and the other costs $2.25 per kg. How much of each type of seed is needed to produce 6 kg at a cost of $8.90?   4 pounds of $1.10 and 2 pounds of $2.25

7. A farmer wants to mix milk containing 6% butterfat with 2 quarts of cream that is 15% butterfat to obtain a mixture that is 12% butterfat. How much milk containing 6% butterfat must he use?   1 quart

8. A store owner has 12 pounds of pasta worth 70¢ a pound. She wants to mix it with pasta worth 45¢ a pound so that the total mixture can be sold for 55¢ a pound (without any gain or loss). How much of the 45¢ pasta must she use?   18 pounds

Page 67

Algebraic Fractions
Problem Solving: Simple Interest and Percent Problems

If $1400 is added to an account earning 6% annually, the interest will amount to $192. How much was in the account originally?
Let x = original account
$.06 (x + 1400) = \$192$
$.06x + 84 = 192$
$.06x = 108$
$x = 1800$ account had $1800

1. How much interest can be earned in one year on $800 at 6%? $48

2. How long will it take $1000 to double at 6% interest?   17 yrs.

3. Sam invested $1600, part at 5% and the rest at 6%. The money earned $85 in one year. How much was invested at 5%?
   Hint:

	P	x	r	x	t	=	I
Amount at 5%	x				1		
Amount at 6%	1600 - x				1		

   $1100

4. The Lewis family invested $900, part at 5% and the rest at 7%. the income from the investment was $58. How much was invested at 7%? $650

5. The Lockmores invested $7000, part at 8% and part at $6\frac{1}{2}$%. If the annual return was $537.50, how much was invested at each rate? $5500 at 8%, $1500 at 6.5%

6. BDLV Associates had $7400 invested at $5\frac{1}{2}$%. After money was withdrawn, $242 was earned on the remaining funds. How much money was withdrawn? $3000

7. Michael has $2000 more invested at $8\frac{1}{2}$% than he does at $9\frac{3}{4}$%. If the annual return from each investment is the same, how much is invested at each rate? $15,600 at 8.5%, $13,600 at 9.75%

8. Ms. Burke invested $53,650, part at 10.5% and the rest at 12%. If the income from the 10.5% investment is one third of that from the 12% investment, how much did she invest at each rate? $14,800 at 10.5%, $38,850 at 12%

Page 68

Answer Key

Algebraic Fractions

Problem Solving: Work Problems

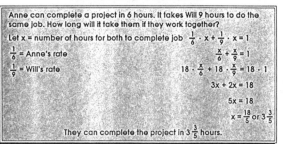

Anne can complete a project in 6 hours. It takes Will 9 hours to do the same job. How long will it take them if they work together?

Let x = number of hours for both to complete job $\frac{1}{6} \cdot x + \frac{1}{9} \cdot x = 1$

$\frac{1}{6}$ = Anne's rate

$\frac{1}{9}$ = Will's rate

$\frac{x}{6} + \frac{x}{9} = 1$

$18 \cdot \frac{x}{6} + 18 \cdot \frac{x}{9} = 18 \cdot 1$

$3x + 2x = 18$

$5x = 18$

$x = \frac{18}{5} \text{ or } 3\frac{3}{5}$

They can complete the project in $3\frac{3}{5}$ hours.

1. Bill can paint a closet in 2 hours. Bob can paint the same closet in 3 hours. How long will it take them to paint the closet working together?
$1\frac{1}{5}$ hrs.

2. Sally can address a box of envelopes in 30 minutes. Her brother Jim can address a box of envelopes in 1 hour. How long would it take both working together to address a box of envelopes? 20 min.

3. Paul can mow the grass in 50 minutes but it takes Dan three times as long. How long will it take them to mow the grass if they work together?
37.5 min.

4. Using 1 drain, a swimming pool can be emptied in 45 minutes. Using a different drain, the job requires 1 hour and 15 minutes. How long will it take if both drains are opened? $28\frac{1}{8}$ min.

5. Susan can sort the office mail in 15 minutes but if Kathy helps, they can sort the mail in 8 minutes. How long would it take Kathy to sort the mail alone? $17\frac{1}{7}$ min.

6. One pipe can fill a tank in 4 hours. A second pipe also requires 4 hours but a third needs three hours. How long will it take to fill the tank if all three pipes are open?
1 hour + 12 min.

Logic Break

☞ Keep in mind...
Refusing to ask for help when you need it is refusing someone the chance to be helpful.

Village Occupations

Clark, Jones, Morgan and Smith are four people whose occupations are salesperson, pharmacist, grocer and police officer, though not necessarily in that order. Use the following statements to determine each person's occupation.

1. Clark and Jones are neighbors and take turns driving each other to work.

2. The grocer makes more money than Morgan.

3. Clark beats Smith regularly at bowling.

4. The salesperson always walks to work.

5. The police officer does not live near Clark.

6. The only time Morgan and the police officer ever met was when Morgan was stopped for speeding.

7. The grocer doesn't bowl.

	Salesperson	Pharmacist	Grocer	Police Officer
Clark		X		
Jones			X	
Morgan	X			
Smith				X

Logic Break

Birthdays

Make your own matrix.

One week there is a birthday party every day. No two children are invited to the same party. Find out the day that each child attends a party. Start your matrix with Sunday and continue through Saturday.

1. Lisa and Pat don't go to a party on a Friday or a Saturday.

2. Pat and Alice don't go on a Tuesday, but Sandy does.

3. Jennifer goes to a party on Wednesday.

4. Jim goes to a party the day after Jennifer.

5. Lisa goes to a party the day before Pat.

6. Paul goes to a party on a Saturday.

	Sat.	Sun.	Mon.	Tues.	Wed.	Thur.	Fri.
Lisa		X					
Pat			X				
Alice							X
Sandy				X			
Jennifer					X		
Jim						X	
Paul	X						

Logic Break

Hobbies

Make your own matrix.

Maureen, Joan, Robert and Bryan each have two favorite hobbies, which include collections. The collections are seashells, stamps, baseball cards, coins, comic books, dolls, bugs and rocks. No two children collect the same things. Find out the two collections each child has.

1. Maureen always finds things for both her collections outdoors.

2. Joan's friend enjoys collecting stamps.

3. One of Bryan's friends enjoys collecting coins.

4. The person who collects comics does not collect baseball cards.

5. One of Bryan's hobbies involves lots of reading.

6. Joan's family has a beach house; this is very helpful for one of her collections.

7. One of the girls collects dolls.

	Seashells	Stamps	Baseball Cards	Coins	Comic Books	Dolls	Bugs	Rocks
Maureen							X	X
Joan	X					X		
Robert			X	X				
Bryan		X			X			

Answer Key

Logic Break

Neighbors

Make your own matrix.

Billy Brown, Willy White, Bobby Blue and George Green all live on the same street. Their houses are painted brown, white, blue and green, but no boy lives in a house that matches his last name. Also, each boy has a pet, and its name does not begin with the same letter as its owner's name. Also, you must find out the location of each house—is it the first, second, third or fourth on the block?

1. George Green owns the bear.

2. Willy White owns the bull.

3. The white house is the last one on the street.

4. Neither the bear nor the bull live next to the first house.

5. Bobby Blue's house is not green.

6. The boy who owns the whale lives in the green house.

7. The gorilla lives in the first house, which is brown.

	brown	white	blue	green	Bear	Bull	Whale	gorilla	first	second	third	fourth
Billy Brown			X		X				X			
Willy White		X				X					X	
Bobby Blue	X						X	X				
George Green		X		X			X					X

Page 73

Linear Equations and Inequalities

☞ Keep in mind...
Minds are like parachutes—they only function when open.

Graphing with Ordered Pairs

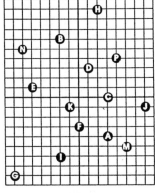

I. Find the coordinates of the indicated point.

1. A $(3, -4)$
2. I $(-2, -6)$
3. H $(2, 9)$
4. C $(3, 0)$
5. E $(-5, 1)$
6. N $(-6, 5)$

II. Name the graph (letter) of each ordered pair.

7. $(-2, 6)$ B
8. $(0, -3)$ F
9. $(5, -5)$ m
10. $(-1, -1)$ K
11. $(-7, -8)$ G
12. $(7, -1)$ J
13. The coordinates are equal.
   K and P
14. The y-coordinate is three times the x-coordinate.
   I and D

III. Name the quadrant or axis on which each point lies.

15. $(-4, 3)$ II
16. $(0, 6)$ y-axis
17. $(4, -2)$ IV
18. $(-1, -1)$ III
19. $(-2, 0)$ x-axis
20. $(1, 2)$ I

Page 74

Linear Equations and Inequalities

Graphing Equations

1. $y = x + 3$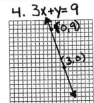
2. $y = -2x + 4$
3. $x + y = 2$

4. $3x + y = 9$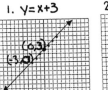
5. $x = -7$
6. $y = -3x + 5$

7. $y = 5 - x$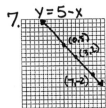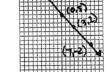
8. $3x + 4y = 12$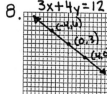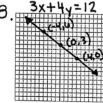

Page 75

Linear Equations and Inequalities

Finding the Slope of a Line

I. Slope = $\frac{\text{vertical change}}{\text{horizontal change}}$

Identify the slope of the line using the graph.

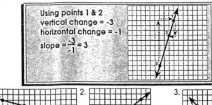

Using points 1 & 2
vertical change = -3
horizontal change = -1
slope = $\frac{-3}{-1}$ = 3

1.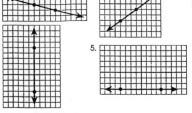
2.
3.
4.
5.

1. $-\frac{1}{4}$
2. $\frac{2}{3}$
3. -1
4. no slope
5. 0 slope

II. Slope = $\frac{\text{change in y-values}}{\text{change in x-values}} = \frac{y_2 - y_1}{x_2 - x_1}$

Find the slope of the line passing through the given points.

$(-1, 5) (3, -2)$
slope = $\frac{-2 - 5}{3 - (-1)} = \frac{-7}{4}$

6. $(0, 0) (3, 5)$ $\frac{5}{3}$
7. $(5, -2) (-7, 4)$ $-\frac{1}{2}$
8. $(-6, 3) (-2, -9)$ -3
9. $(6, -9) (-4, 3)$ $-\frac{6}{5}$
10. $(-3, -11) (2, -7)$ $\frac{4}{5}$
11. $(7, 3) (-8, 3)$ 0 slope
12. $(0, 0) (4, -3)$ $-\frac{3}{4}$
13. $(-2, -3) (2, 5)$ $\frac{2}{1}$
14. $(-4, 8) (-4, -3)$ no slope

Page 76

Algebra IF8762 121 © MCMXCIV Instructional Fair, Inc.

Answer Key

Page 77

Linear Equations and Inequalities

Slope-Intercept Form

$$4x + y = 3$$
$$4x - 4x + y = -4x + 3$$
$$y = -4x + 3$$

I. Solve for y.
1. $x + y = 3$ $y = -x + 3$
2. $2x - y = 7$ $y = 2x - 7$
3. $-6 + 2y = 10x$ $y = 5x + 3$
4. $3y - 6x + 12 = 0$ $y = 2x - 4$

$$9x - 3y = -6$$
$$y = 3x + 2$$
$$m = \frac{3}{1}$$
$$y_0 = 2$$

II. Solve for y, state the m and y_0.
5. $2y - 6x = 2$ $y = 3x + 1, m = 3/1, y_0 = 1$
6. $y - 4x = -3$ $y = 4x - 3, m = \frac{4}{1}, y_0 = -3$
7. $4y = 5x + 12$ $y = \frac{5}{4}x + 3, m = \frac{5}{4}, y_0 = 3$
8. $2x - 3y = 5$ $y = \frac{2}{3}x - \frac{5}{3}, m = \frac{2}{3}, y_0 = -\frac{5}{3}$

III. Graph the line by 1.) solving for y 2.) using m and y_0.
9. $4x + y = -8$ $m = -\frac{4}{1}$ $y_0 = -8$ (0,-8)
10. $y - 3x = -9$ $m = \frac{3}{1}$ $y_0 = -9$ (0,-9)
11. $2x - 4y = -16$ $m = \frac{1}{2}$ $y_0 = 4$ (0,4)
12. $3x + 3y + 4 = 0$ $m = -\frac{1}{1}$ $y_0 = -\frac{4}{3}$ (0,-1)

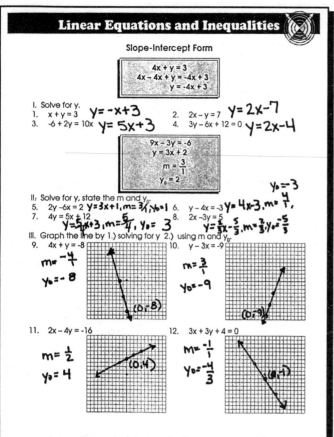

Page 77

Page 78

Linear Equations and Inequalities

...More Slope-Intercept Form

Graph from the slope-intercept form: $y = mx + b$.   m = slope   b = y-intercept

$y = 4x + 2$
1) Plot y-intercept
   $b = 2 \Rightarrow (0, 2)$
2) Find other points using slope
   $m = 4 \Rightarrow \frac{4}{1}$ or $\frac{-4}{-1}$
3) Connect points.

1. $y = 2x - 4$ (2,0) (0,-4)
2. $3x - y = 7$ (3,2) (0,-7)
3. $2x + 3y = 6$ (0,2) (3,0)
4. $y = -\frac{3}{2}x + 1$ (0,1) (4,-5)
5. $x - 4y + 8 = 0$ (-8,0) (0,2)
6. $6x - 5y = 15$ (5,3) (0,-3)

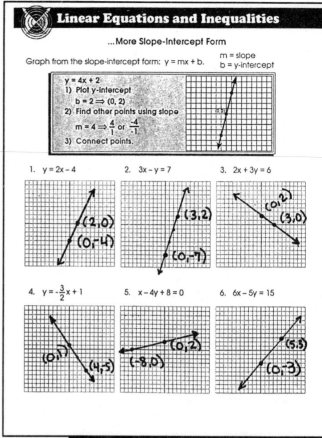

Page 78

Page 79

Linear Equations and Inequalities

X and Y Intercepts

I. Find the x and y intercepts.

$$2x + y = 3$$
To find x intercept, let y = 0. To find y-intercept, let x = 0.
$2x + 0 = 3$ $2 \cdot 0 + y = 3$
$2x = 3$ $y = 3$ (0, 3)
$x = \frac{3}{2}$ $\left(\frac{3}{2}, 0\right)$

1. $3x + 4y = 12$
2. $4x + y = 2$
3. $5x - 4y = 15$
4. $2x - 2y = -4$
5. $3x + y = -9$
6. $4x - 2y - 8 = 0$

II. Find the x and y intercepts. Then graph.
7. $x + 2y = 5$ $x_0 = 5$ $y_0 = 2.5$ (0,2.5) (5,0)
8. $2x - 5y = 0$ $x_0 = 0$ $y_0 = 0$ (5,2)
9. $4x - 3y = -2$ $x_0 = -\frac{1}{2}$ $y_0 = \frac{2}{3}$ $\left(\frac{2}{3}\right)$ $\left(-\frac{1}{2}\right)$
10. $3x + 2y = 6$ $x_0 = 2$ $y_0 = 3$ (0,3) (2,0)
11. $5x - 7y = 12$ $x_0 = \frac{12}{5}$ $y_0 = -1\frac{5}{7}$ $\left(0, -\frac{12}{7}\right)$ $\left(\frac{12}{5}, 0\right)$
12. $8x + 10y = 50$ $x_0 = 2\frac{3}{4}$ $y_0 = 5$ (0,5) $\left(\frac{25}{4}, 0\right)$

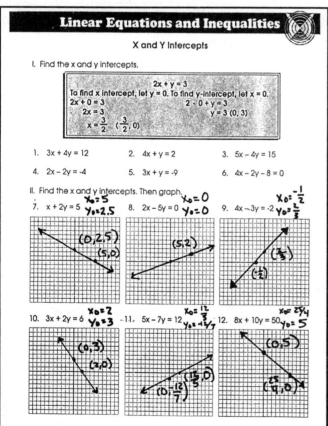

Page 79

Page 80

Linear Equations and Inequalities

Writing an Equation of a Line in Standard Form: Ax + By = C

I. Put in standard form.

$y = -\frac{2}{5}x + 3$
$-5y = 2x - 15$
$-2x - 5y = -15$
$2x + 5y = 15$

1. $y = -\frac{3}{4}x + 2$ $3x + 4y = 8$
2. $y = \frac{1}{2}x - 2$ $x - 2y = 4$
3. $y = 3x + 6$ $3x - y = -6$
4. $y = -x - 5$ $x + y = -5$
5. $y = \frac{3}{4}x + \frac{1}{2}$ $3x - 4y = -2$
6. $y = -\frac{1}{4}x + 8$ $x + 4y = 32$

II. Find the equation of a line in standard form using the slope-intercept form.

$m = -\frac{3}{4}$ $y_0 = 2$
$y = -\frac{3}{4}x + 2$
$\frac{3}{4}x + y = 2$
$3x + 4y = 8$

7. $m = 3$ $y_0 = -\frac{1}{2}$ $6x - 2y = 1$
8. $m = \frac{5}{4}$ $y_0 = 2$ $5x - 4y = 8$
9. $m = -\frac{2}{3}$ $y_0 = \frac{3}{5}$ $10x + 15y = 9$
10. $m = 4$ $y_0 = -3$ $4x - y = 3$
11. $m = \frac{3}{4}$ $y_0 = \frac{1}{2}$ $3x - 4y = -2$
12. $m = \frac{7}{2}$ $y_0 = -\frac{3}{4}$ $14x - 4y = 3$
13. $m = 0$ $y_0 = -3$ $y = -3$

Page 80

Answer Key

Linear Equations and Inequalities

Linear Equations and Inequalities

...More Writing an Equation of a Line in Standard Form: Ax + By = C

III. Find the equation of the line in standard form using the point-slope formula.

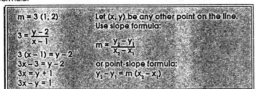

$$m = 3 \, (1, 2) \qquad \text{Let } (x, y) \text{ be any other point on the line.}$$
$$3 = \frac{y-2}{x-1} \qquad \text{Use slope formula:}$$
$$3(x-1) = y - 2 \qquad m = \frac{y_2 - y_1}{x_2 - x_1}$$
$$3x - 3 = y - 2 \qquad \text{or point-slope formula:}$$
$$3x = y + 1 \qquad y_2 - y_1 = m(x_2 - x_1)$$
$$3x - y = 1$$

1. m = -3, (4, 5)
$$3x + y = 17$$

2. m = -2, (1, 3)
$$2x + y = 5$$

3. m = 0, (4, -6)
$$y = -6$$

4. $m = \frac{3}{4}$, (1, 0)
$$3x - 4y = 3$$

5. no slope, $(-3, \frac{3}{4})$
$$x = -3$$

6. m = -1, (-1, 4)
$$x + y = 3$$

7. $m = -\frac{1}{2}$, (6, -3)
$$x + 2y = 0$$

8. m = 1, (1, -4)
$$x - y = 5$$

9. $m = \frac{1}{4}$, (-4, 3)
$$x - 4y = -16$$

10. $m = \frac{1}{3}$, (-3, -2)
$$x - 3y = 3$$

11. $m = \frac{2}{3}$, (-1, 1)
$$2x - 3y = -5$$

12. m = 0, (7, -4)
$$y = -4$$

13. $m = -\frac{2}{1}$, (-2, -7)
$$2x + y = -11$$

14. $m = \frac{5}{1}$, (-2, 0)
$$5x - y = -10$$

Page 81

Linear Equations and Inequalities

...More Writing an Equation of a Line in Standard Form: Ax + By = C

IV. Find the equation of the line in standard form using 1) slope and then 2) point-slope formula.

$$(-3, 4) \, (4, 7)$$
$$m = \frac{7-4}{4-(-3)} = \frac{3}{7}$$
$$\frac{3}{7} = \frac{y-7}{x-4}$$
$$y - 4 = \frac{3}{7}(x + 3)$$
$$7y - 28 = 3x + 9$$
$$3x - 7y = -37$$

1. (2, 1)   (4, 0)
$$y + 2y = 4$$

2. (5, 2)   (2, -1)
$$x - y = 3$$

3. (4, -3)   (0, 3)
$$3x + 2y = 6$$

4. (-2, -3)   (-1, 2)
$$5x - y = -7$$

5. (0, 0)   (-1, -2)
$$2x - y = 0$$

6. (6, -3)   (-2, -3)
$$y = -3$$

7. (2, 3)   (-1, 5)
$$2x + 3y = 13$$

8. (4, 8)   (4, -2)
$$x = 4$$

9. (5, 8)   (3, 2)
$$3x - y = 7$$

10. (-2, 5)   (3, -10)
$$3x + y = -1$$

11. (0, 2)   (-4, 2)
$$y = 2$$

12. (-1, -1)   (0, -4)
$$3x + y = -4$$

13. (-3, 6)   (-3, 2)
$$x = -3$$

14. (-6, 6)   (3, 3)
$$x + 3y = 12$$

Page 82

Linear Equations and Inequalities

Graphing Linear Inequalities

$$y < -\frac{1}{2}x + 1$$

1.) Graph $y = -\frac{1}{2}x + 1$ as a dotted line.
2.) Choose a point in one half-plane and substitute. Try (0, 3):
$$3 < -\frac{1}{2} \cdot 0 + 1 = 3 < 1 = \text{False}$$
3.) Shade half-plane that does not contain (0, 3).

$$3x - 4y \leq 12 \Rightarrow y \geq \frac{3}{4}x - 3$$

1.) Graph $y \geq \frac{3}{4}x - 3$ as a solid line.
2.) Choose a point in one half-plane and substitute. Try (0, 0):
$$0 \geq \frac{3}{4} \cdot -3 \Rightarrow 0 \geq -3 \Rightarrow \text{True}$$
3.) Shade the half-plane that contains (0, 0).

1. y > x + 1
2. 3x - y ≤ 6
3. y + 5 ≤ 0
4. y ≥ 2x - 3
5. x + y < 3
6. 2x + y > -8

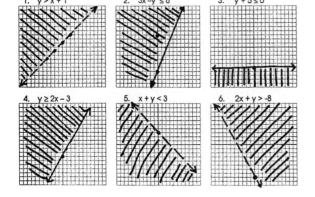

Page 83

Linear Equations and Inequalities

Systems of Equations: Graphic Method

Solve by graphing.

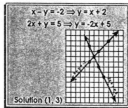

$$x - y = -2 \Rightarrow y = x + 2$$
$$2x + y = 5 \Rightarrow y = -2x + 5$$

Solution (1, 3)

1. x - y = 6
   2x + y = 0

2. 2x - 2y = -4
   y = 2

3. 2x - y = 1
   3x + y = -6

4. x + 2y = 4
   2x - y = 8

5. 2x - y = 5
   x - y = 1

6. x = 3
   y = -2

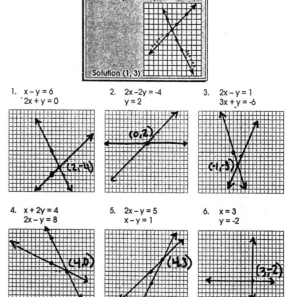

Page 84

Answer Key

Linear Equations and Inequalities

Systems of Equations: Elimination Method

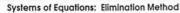

$$
\begin{array}{ll}
x + y = 6 & x + y = 6 \\
x - y = 4 & \underline{+x - y = 4} \\
& \dfrac{2x = 10}{x = 5}
\end{array}
$$

$$
\begin{array}{l}
x + y = 6 \Rightarrow 5 + y = 6 \\
y = 1 \\
\text{Solution } (5, 1)
\end{array}
$$

$$
\begin{array}{ll}
3y = -7x + 7 \Rightarrow & 7x + 3y = 7 \\
2y = 7x - 7 \Rightarrow & \underline{- (7x - 2y = 7)} \\
& 5y = 0 \\
& y = 0
\end{array}
$$

$$
\begin{array}{l}
2y = 7x - 7 \Rightarrow 0 = 7x - 7 \\
7 = 7x \\
1 = X \\
\text{Solution } (1, 0)
\end{array}
$$

1. $2x + y = -6$
   $3x + y = -10$ $(-4, 2)$

2. $8x - y = 20$
   $-5x + y = -8$ $(4, 12)$

3. $2x + y = 0$
   $2x - 3y = -8$ $(-1, 2)$

4. $5x + 3y = 10$
   $2x - 3y = 4$ $(2, 0)$

5. $9x - 3y = 9$
   $x + 3y = 11$ $(2, 3)$

6. $x + 3y = 9$
   $x - 2y = -6$ $(0, 3)$

7. $2x + y = 4$
   $2x + 2y = 2$ $(3, -2)$

8. $7y + 15 = 3x$
   $15 = 3x + 2y$ $(5, 0)$

9. $25x = 91 - 16y$
   $16y = 64 - 16x$ $(3, 1)$

10. $4x - 2y = -2$
    $4x + 3y = -12$ $\left(-\dfrac{3}{2}, -2\right)$

11. $2x + y = -7$
    $y = 3x + 3$ $(-2, -3)$

12. $3x = -2y + 10$
    $x = 2y + 6$ $(4, -1)$

13. $x + 4y = 2$
    $x - 2y = 8$ $(6, -1)$

14. $x + 5y + 11 = 0$
    $3x - 5y - 7 = 0$ $(-1, -2)$

Page 85

Linear Equations and Inequalities

Systems of Equations: More Elimination Method

$$
\begin{array}{ll}
2x + 5y = 11 & 4x + 10y = 22 \\
3x - 2y = -12 & \underline{+ 15x - 10y = -60} \\
& \dfrac{19x = -38}{x = -2}
\end{array}
$$

Solution $(-2, 3)$

1. $3x - y = 3$
   $x + 3y = 11$ $(2, 3)$

2. $4x + 2y = 14$
   $3x - y = 8$ $(3, 1)$

3. $4x - y = 9$
   $3x - 5y = 11$ $(2, -1)$

4. $2x + 2y = -16$
   $4x - 4y = 32$ $(0, -8)$

5. $3x - 5y = 11$
   $4x + 3y = 5$ $(2, -1)$

6. $2x - 7y = 8$
   $3x - 4y = -1$ $(-3, -2)$

7. $5x - 2y = 4$
   $3x - 4y = -6$ $(2, 3)$

8. $6x + 5y = -2$
   $2x + 3y = 6$ $\left(-\dfrac{9}{2}, 5\right)$

9. $2x + 3y = 4$
   $5x + 4y = 3$ $(-1, 2)$

10. $5x - 2y = 17$
    $2x + 3y = 3$ $(3, -1)$

11. $x - 2y = -8$
    $3x + y = 4$ $(0, 4)$

12. $3x + 5y = 9$
    $9x + 2y = -12$ $(-2, 3)$

13. $2x + 3y = 14$
    $-2y + 3x = -5$ $(1, 4)$

14. $5x + 2y = -8$
    $2x - 5y = -9$ $(-2, 1)$

Page 86

Linear Equations and Inequalities

Systems of Equations: Substitution Method

$$
\begin{array}{ll}
x - 5y = 10 & x - 5(2x + 7) = 10 \\
-2x + y = 7 \Rightarrow y = 2x + 7 & x - 10x - 35 = 10 \\
\text{Solution } (-5, -3) & -9x - 35 = 10 \\
& -9x = 45 \\
& x = -5
\end{array}
$$

1. $y = 5 - 4x$
   $3x - 2y = 12$ $(2, -3)$

2. $3x + 2y = 8$
   $x = 3y + 10$ $(4, -2)$

3. $3x - 4y = -15$
   $5x + y = -2$ $(-1, 3)$

4. $x + y = 2$
   $3x + 2y = 5$ $(1, 1)$

5. $x = 3 - 3y$
   $4y = x + 11$ $(-3, 2)$

6. $x - y = -15$
   $x + y = -5$ $(-5, 10)$

7. $2x + y = -6$
   $3x - 2y = -10$ $(-4, 2)$

8. $y = -x + 6$
   $x - 2y = -6$ $(2, 4)$

9. $2y - x = 6$
   $3y - x = 4$ $(-10, -2)$

10. $5x - 6y = 16$
    $5x + y = 2$ $\left(\dfrac{4}{5}, -2\right)$

11. $y = 3x$
    $x + y = 8$ $(2, 6)$

12. $x - 3y = -5$
    $2x + y = 11$ $(4, 3)$

13. $-x + y = 5$
    $y = -3x + 1$ $(-1, 4)$

14. $2x = 3y$
    $x = 3y - 3$ $(3, 2)$

Page 87

Linear Equations and Inequalities

Solving Problems with Two Variables

Set up and solve each equation.

> If 8 pens and 7 pencils cost $3.37 while 5 pens and 11 pencils cost $3.10, how much does each pen and each pencil cost?
>
> Let x = cost of 1 pen   Let y = cost of 1 pencil $8x + 7 \cdot 15 = 337$
> $8x + 7y = 337$ $-40x - 35y = -1685$ $8x + 105 = 337$
> $5x + 11y = 310$ $\underline{40x + 88y = 2480}$ $8x = 232$
> $53y = 795$ $x = 29$
> $y = 15$
>
> Pens cost $.29 and pencils cost $.15.

1. A rectangle has a perimeter of 18 cm. Its length is 5 cm greater than its width. Find the dimensions. 2×7

2. Timmy has 180 marbles, some plain and some colored. If there are 32 more plain marbles than colored marbles, how many colored marbles does he have? 74

3. A theater sold 900 tickets to a play. Floor seats cost $12 each and balcony seats $10 each. Total receipts were $9780. How many of each type of ticket were sold? 390 floor + 510 balcony

4. Ryan and Karl spent 28 hours building a tree house. Ryan worked 4 more hours than Karl. How many hours did each work? Karl 12 hrs., Ryan 16 hrs.

5. The difference between seven times one number and three times a second number is 25. The sum of twice the first and five times the second is 95. Find the numbers. 10 and 15

6. The sum of two numbers is 36. Their difference is 6. Find the numbers. $21 + 15$

7. The volleyball club has 41 members. There are 3 more boys than girls. How many girls are there? 19

8. The sum of two numbers is 15. Twice one number equals 3 times the other. Find the numbers. 6 and 9

Page 88

Answer Key

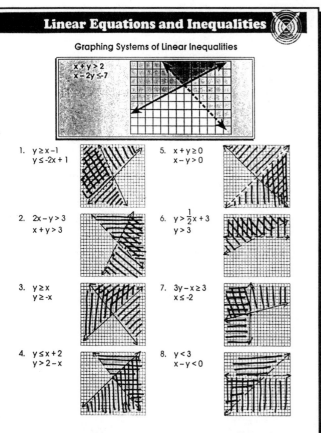

$$x + y > 2$$
$$x - 2y \leq -7$$

1. $y \geq x - 1$
   $y \leq -2x + 1$

2. $2x - y > 3$
   $x + y > 3$

3. $y \geq x$
   $y \geq -x$

4. $y \leq x + 2$
   $y > 2 - x$

5. $x + y \geq 0$
   $x - y > 0$

6. $y > \frac{1}{2}x + 3$
   $y > 3$

7. $3y - x \geq 3$
   $x \leq -2$

8. $y < 3$
   $x - y < 0$

Try and de-code these words and phrases.

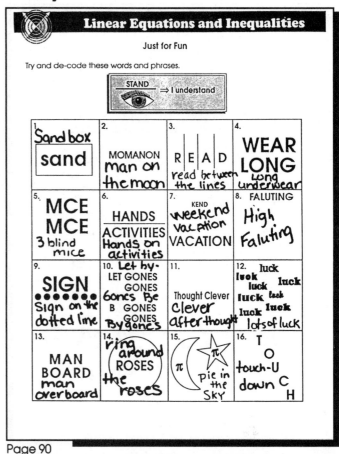

STAND / eye ⇒ I understand

1. Sand box — sand
2. MOMANON — man on the moon
3. R E A D — read between the lines
4. WEAR LONG — long underwear
5. MCE MCE — 3 blind mice
6. HANDS ACTIVITIES — Hands on activities
7. KEND weekend vacation VACATION — weekend vacation
8. FALUTING High — High Faluting
9. SIGN — Sign on the dotted line
10. Let hy- LET GONES GONES Bones Be B GONES GONES Bygones — Let bygones be bygones
11. Thought Clever Clever afterthought — Clever afterthought
12. luck — lots of luck
13. MAN BOARD — man overboard
14. ring around ROSES the roses — ring around the roses
15. π pie in the sky — pie in the sky
16. T O touch-U down C H — touchdown

☞ Keep in mind...
You can forget your own problems if you can help someone solve theirs.

Simplifying Radicals

All variables are non-negative numbers.

$$\sqrt{18x^3y^2} = \sqrt{9 \cdot 2 \cdot x^2 \cdot x \cdot y^2}$$
$$= 3xy\sqrt{2x}$$

1. $\sqrt{100}$ — 10

2. $\sqrt{75}$ — $5\sqrt{3}$

3. $-\sqrt{144a^2}$ — $-12a$

4. $\sqrt{128x^3}$ — $8x\sqrt{2x}$

5. $2\sqrt{1000}$ — $20\sqrt{10}$

6. $\sqrt{15a^9b}$ — $a^4\sqrt{15b}$

7. $\sqrt{16c^2d^2}$ — $4cd$

8. $2\sqrt{27x^5y}$ — $6x^2\sqrt{3xy}$

9. $-\sqrt{20xy^2}$ — $-2y\sqrt{5x}$

10. $\sqrt{50a^3}$ — $5a\sqrt{2a}$

11. $\sqrt{96bc^2d^5}$ — $4cd^2\sqrt{6bd}$

12. $-3\sqrt{150a^7c^2}$ — $-15a^3c\sqrt{6a}$

13. $\sqrt{27a^2}$ — $3a\sqrt{3}$

14. $2\sqrt{50x^2yz^3}$ — $10xz\sqrt{2yz}$

15. $\sqrt{243m^5n^2}$ — $9m^2n\sqrt{3m}$

16. $-\sqrt{320y^8z^{10}}$ — $-8y^4z^5\sqrt{5y}$

All variables are non-negative numbers.

Products — Multiply radicands and simplify.

$$4\sqrt{3} \cdot 2\sqrt{18} = 8\sqrt{54} = 8\sqrt{9} \cdot 6 = 8 \cdot 3\sqrt{6} = 24\sqrt{6}$$
$$\sqrt{2a} \cdot \sqrt{6a} = \sqrt{12a^2} = \sqrt{4 \cdot 3} \cdot a^2 = 2a\sqrt{3}$$

1. $\sqrt{2} \cdot \sqrt{8}$ — 4

2. $5\sqrt{5} \cdot 3\sqrt{14}$ — $15\sqrt{70}$

3. $\sqrt{5b} \cdot \sqrt{10b}$ — $5b\sqrt{2}$

4. $a\sqrt{2x} \cdot x\sqrt{6x}$ — $2ax^2\sqrt{3}$

5. $2m\sqrt{7mn} \cdot 3\sqrt{7m}$ — $42m^2\sqrt{n}$

6. $-5a\sqrt{2a^4b} \cdot 4b\sqrt{12a^5b^4}$ — $-40a^4b^3\sqrt{6ab}$

7. $2\sqrt{5}(-\sqrt{3x})$ — $-2\sqrt{15x}$

8. $5\sqrt{6} \cdot 2\sqrt{2}$ — $20\sqrt{3}$

9. $\sqrt{x} \cdot \sqrt{9x}$ — $3x$

10. $\sqrt{2x} \cdot \sqrt{10x^2y}$ — $2x\sqrt{5xy}$

11. $4x\sqrt{5} \cdot \sqrt{8xy^2}$ — $8xy\sqrt{10x}$

12. $2\sqrt{x^3} \cdot 4\sqrt{x}$ — $8x^2$

13. $-7\sqrt{3y} \cdot \sqrt{6y}$ — $-21y\sqrt{2}$

14. $\sqrt{xy} \cdot \sqrt{xy}$ — xy

Answer Key

Quotients of Radicals

Quotients—Rationalizing the denominator.

$$\sqrt{\tfrac{7}{8}} = \frac{\sqrt{7}}{\sqrt{8}} = \frac{\sqrt{2}}{\sqrt{2}} = \frac{\sqrt{14}}{\sqrt{16}} = \frac{\sqrt{14}}{4}$$

$$\sqrt{\frac{2a^4b^3}{27x^3}} = \frac{\sqrt{2a^4b^3}}{\sqrt{27x^3}} = \frac{\sqrt{3x}}{\sqrt{3x}} = \frac{\sqrt{6a^4b^3x}}{\sqrt{81x^4}} = \frac{a^2b\sqrt{6bx}}{9x^2}$$

1. $\sqrt{\dfrac{2ab^2}{c^2d}}$ $\dfrac{b\sqrt{2ad}}{cd}$

8. $\sqrt{\dfrac{8}{25}}$ $\dfrac{2\sqrt{2}}{5}$

2. $\sqrt{\dfrac{2x}{3y}}$ $\dfrac{\sqrt{6xy}}{3y}$

9. $\dfrac{3\sqrt{2}}{\sqrt{3}}$ $\sqrt{6}$

3. $\sqrt{\dfrac{19x^2}{32}}$ $\dfrac{x\sqrt{38}}{8}$

10. $\sqrt{\dfrac{4x^2}{25}}$ $\dfrac{2x}{5}$

4. $\sqrt{\dfrac{4a^2b}{x^6y^7}}$ $\dfrac{2a\sqrt{by}}{x^4y^4}$

11. $\sqrt{\dfrac{11y^3}{9}}$ $\dfrac{y\sqrt{11y}}{3}$

5. $x\sqrt{\dfrac{5d}{3x^2}}$ $\dfrac{\sqrt{15d}}{3}$

12. $\sqrt{\dfrac{25}{3x}}$ $\dfrac{5\sqrt{3x}}{3x}$

6. $\sqrt{\dfrac{7a^2}{8cd}}$ $\dfrac{a\sqrt{14cd}}{4cd}$

13. $\sqrt{\dfrac{3}{6x^3}}$ $\dfrac{\sqrt{2x}}{2x^2}$

7. $\sqrt{\dfrac{n^2}{7}}$ $\dfrac{n\sqrt{7}}{7}$

14. $\dfrac{\sqrt{8x^2y}}{\sqrt{2y}}$ $2x$

Page 93

Sums and Differences of Radicals

$$3\sqrt{9xy^2} - y\sqrt{16xy^2} + 2y^2\sqrt{25x} = 9y^2\sqrt{x} - 4y^2\sqrt{x} + 10y^2\sqrt{x} = 15y^2\sqrt{x}$$
$$10\sqrt{\tfrac{1}{5}} + 4\sqrt{18} + 3\sqrt{45} - 8\sqrt{\tfrac{1}{2}} = 2\sqrt{5} + 12\sqrt{2} + 9\sqrt{5} - 4\sqrt{2} = 11\sqrt{5} + 8\sqrt{2}$$

1. $3\sqrt{7} - 4\sqrt{7} + 2\sqrt{7}$
$$\sqrt{7}$$

8. $\sqrt{50} + \sqrt{98} - \sqrt{75} + \sqrt{27}$
$$12\sqrt{2} - 2\sqrt{3}$$

2. $4\sqrt{27} - 2\sqrt{48} + \sqrt{147}$
$$11\sqrt{3}$$

9. $2x\sqrt{ab} - 2y\sqrt{ab} + 4x\sqrt{ab}$
$$(6x-2y)\sqrt{ab} \text{ or } 2(3x-y)\sqrt{ab}$$

3. $5\sqrt{3} - 4\sqrt{7} - 3\sqrt{3} + \sqrt{7}$
$$2\sqrt{3} - 3\sqrt{7}$$

10. $2b\sqrt{3c} + b\sqrt{5c} + b\sqrt{3c} - 2b\sqrt{5c}$
$$3b\sqrt{3c} - b\sqrt{5c}$$

4. $5\sqrt{x} - 3\sqrt{x} + a\sqrt{x}$
$$(a+2)\sqrt{x}$$

11. $4\sqrt{c^3d^3} + 3cd\sqrt{4cd} - 2c\sqrt{9cd^3}$
$$4cd\sqrt{cd}$$

5. $4\sqrt{\tfrac{1}{2}} + 2\sqrt{18} - 6\sqrt{\tfrac{2}{9}}$
$$6\sqrt{2}$$

12. $8\sqrt{12} - 10\sqrt{\tfrac{1}{5}} - 108 + \sqrt{125}$
$$-108 + 16\sqrt{3} + 3\sqrt{5}$$

6. $\sqrt{63} - \sqrt{28} - \sqrt{7}$
$$0$$

13. $x\sqrt{4x} + \sqrt{x^3}$
$$3x\sqrt{x}$$

7. $6\sqrt{3} - 2\sqrt{75} + 4\sqrt{\tfrac{3}{16}}$
$$-9\sqrt{3}$$

14. $3x\sqrt{7} + \sqrt{28x^2} - \sqrt{63x^2}$
$$2x\sqrt{7}$$

Page 94

Combined Operations with Radicals

1. $\sqrt{\dfrac{8}{9}} + 2\sqrt{\dfrac{1}{2}} - 3\sqrt{\dfrac{9}{8}}$
$$\dfrac{-7\sqrt{2}}{12}$$

8. $\sqrt{100x} - \sqrt{9x}$
$$7\sqrt{x}$$

2. $3\sqrt{2x^3} - \sqrt{8x^3}$
$$x\sqrt{2x}$$

9. $\sqrt{12y^3} - 2\sqrt{3y^3} + \sqrt{27y^3}$
$$3y\sqrt{3y}$$

3. $\sqrt{3}(\sqrt{3} + 2)$
$$3 + 2\sqrt{3}$$

10. $\sqrt{25 - \dfrac{25}{4}}$
$$\dfrac{5\sqrt{3}}{2}$$

4. $\sqrt{7}(8 + \sqrt{12})$
$$8\sqrt{7} + 2\sqrt{21}$$

11. $\sqrt{\dfrac{60m^3n}{5m}}$
$$2m\sqrt{3n}$$

5. $\sqrt{5}(\sqrt{2} - \sqrt{3})$
$$\sqrt{10} - \sqrt{15}$$

12. $2x\sqrt{25x} + x\sqrt{4x} - 3x\sqrt{9x}$
$$3x\sqrt{x}$$

6. $(\sqrt{5} - 2)(\sqrt{5} + 2)$
$$1$$

13. $\dfrac{2}{\sqrt{6} - 3}$
$$\dfrac{2\sqrt{6} + 6}{-3}$$

7. $(8 + \sqrt{3})(8 - \sqrt{3})$
$$61$$

14. $\dfrac{4}{-2 + \sqrt{7}}$
$$\dfrac{-8 - 4\sqrt{7}}{-3}$$

Page 95

Solving Radical Equations

$$3 + \sqrt{x} = 6 \qquad \sqrt{x} = 3 \qquad (\sqrt{x})^2 = (3)^2 \qquad x = 9$$

1. $\sqrt{x - 1} = 4$
$$\{17\}$$

8. $4 + \sqrt{x + 1} = 5$
$$\{0\}$$

2. $4 = 5\sqrt{x}$
$$\left\{\dfrac{16}{25}\right\}$$

9. $\dfrac{\sqrt{5 - 2x}}{3} = 1$
$$\{-2\}$$

3. $\sqrt{x + 3} = 1$
$$\{-2\}$$

10. $\sqrt{4x - 3} = \sqrt{x}$
$$\{1\}$$

4. $8 = \sqrt{5a + 1}$
$$\left\{\dfrac{63}{5}\right\}$$

11. $5 = \dfrac{15}{\sqrt{2a - 3}}$
$$\{6\}$$

5. $2\sqrt{x} = 5$
$$\left\{\dfrac{25}{4}\right\}$$

12. $6 - \sqrt{y - 5} = 3$
$$\{14\}$$

6. $\sqrt{7 + 3x} = 4$
$$\{3\}$$

13. $2\sqrt{5} = 3\sqrt{x}$
$$\left\{\dfrac{20}{9}\right\}$$

7. $\sqrt{4 - x} = 7$
$$\{-45\}$$

14. $2\sqrt{x} = 4\sqrt{3}$
$$\{12\}$$

Page 96

Answer Key

Solving Quadratic Equations

$$(x-5)^2 = 36$$
$$\sqrt{(x-5)^2} = \sqrt{36}$$
$$x-5 = \pm 6$$
$$x = 11, -1$$

1. $x^2 = 25$ $\{-5, 5\}$

2. $(x-2)^2 = 9$ $\{-1, 5\}$

3. $2y^2 = 32$ $\{-4, 4\}$

4. $x^2 - 49 = 0$ $\{-7, 7\}$

5. $3a^2 - 1 = 11$ $\{-2, 2\}$

6. $(2x-5)^2 = 49$ $\{-1, 6\}$

7. $(x+1)^2 = 4$ $\{-3, 1\}$

8. $(x+17)^2 = 49$ $\{-24, -10\}$

9. $(x+3)^2 = 0$ $\{-3\}$

10. $4(y+5)^2 = 4$ $\{-6, -4\}$

11. $(2x-6)^2 = 16$ $\{1, 5\}$

12. $3(2y+7)^2 = 27$ $\{-5, -2\}$

The Quadratic Formula

$$x = \frac{-b \pm \sqrt{b^2 - 4ac}}{2a}$$
$$3x^2 - 5x - 4 = 0$$
$$a = 3, \ b = -5, \ c = -4 \Rightarrow \frac{5 \pm \sqrt{25 - 4(3)(-4)}}{6} = \frac{5 \pm \sqrt{73}}{6}$$

Solve using the quadratic formula.

1. $x^2 - 2x - 8 = 0$ $\{-2, 4\}$

2. $y^2 + 11y + 10 = 0$ $\{-10, -1\}$

3. $x^2 + 2x - 4 = 0$ $\{-1 \pm \sqrt{5}\}$

4. $y^2 + 5y - 7 = 0$ $\left\{\dfrac{-5 \pm \sqrt{53}}{2}\right\}$

5. $2x^2 - 3x - 5 = 0$ $\left\{-1, 2\frac{1}{2}\right\}$

6. $2y^2 + 4y = 1$ $\left\{\dfrac{-2 \pm \sqrt{6}}{2}\right\}$

7. $7x^2 + 4x - 5 = 0$ $\left\{\dfrac{-2 \pm \sqrt{39}}{7}\right\}$

8. $3x^2 + 10x + 5 = 0$ $\left\{\dfrac{-5 \pm \sqrt{10}}{3}\right\}$

9. $2y^2 = 3y + 4$ $\left\{\dfrac{3 \pm \sqrt{41}}{4}\right\}$

10. $8x^2 + 7x - 2 = 0$ $\left\{\dfrac{-7 \pm \sqrt{113}}{16}\right\}$

11. $x^2 = 4x$ $\{0, 4\}$

12. $\dfrac{3}{x-1} - 4 = \dfrac{1}{x+1}$ $\left\{\dfrac{1 \pm \sqrt{33}}{4}\right\}$

Completing the Square

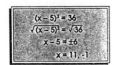

$$x^2 + 2x - 5 = 0$$
$$x^2 + 2x + 1 = 5 + 1$$
$$(x+1)^2 = 6$$
$$x + 1 = \pm \sqrt{6}$$
$$x = -1 \pm \sqrt{6}$$

Solve by completing the square.

1. $y^2 + 10y - 11 = 0$ $\{-11, 1\}$

2. $x^2 + 4x - 12 = 0$ $\{-6, 2\}$

3. $y^2 + 6y = -8$ $\{-4, -2\}$

4. $x^2 - 14x + 40 = 0$ $\{4, 10\}$

5. $x^2 - 16x = -60$ $\{6, 10\}$

6. $4x^2 - 17x + 4 = 0$  $\left\{\frac{1}{4}, 4\right\}$

7. $2a^2 - 2a - 1 = 0$ $\left\{\dfrac{1 \pm \sqrt{3}}{2}\right\}$

8. $x^2 = -5x + 3$ $\left\{\dfrac{-5 \pm \sqrt{37}}{2}\right\}$

9. $y^2 - 7y - 9 = 0$ $\left\{\dfrac{7 \pm \sqrt{85}}{2}\right\}$

10. $2x = 5 + \dfrac{4}{x}$ $\left\{\dfrac{5 \pm \sqrt{57}}{4}\right\}$

Problem Solving with Quadratic Equations

1. Two consecutive, positive, odd numbers have a product of 675. What are the numbers?

   $25, 27$

2. The sum of the squares of two consecutive, positive, odd numbers is 74. What is the number?

   $5, 7$

3. The perimeter of a rectangular pool is 32 meters, and its area is 48 square meters. What are its dimensions?

   4×12

4. The sum of the squares of two consecutive, positive numbers is 85. Find the numbers.

   $5 \ \& \ 7$

5. A rectangular piece of artwork is 4 meters wide and 6 meters long. It is surrounded by a uniform sidewalk. If the area of the sidewalk is 39 square meters, how wide is the sidewalk?

   $1\frac{1}{2}m$

6. There are two positive numbers such that one is 6 less than twice the other. The difference of the squares of the two numbers is 1311. Find the numbers.

   $25 \ \& \ 44$

Answer Key

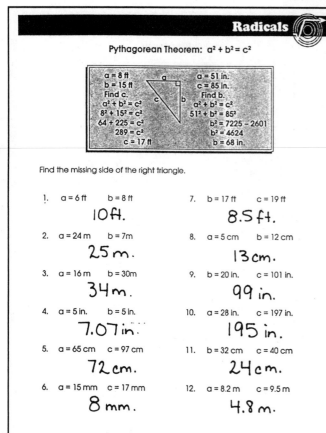

Radicals

Pythagorean Theorem: $a^2 + b^2 = c^2$

a = 8 ft
b = 15 ft
Find c.
$a^2 + b^2 = c^2$
$8^2 + 15^2 = c^2$
$64 + 225 = c^2$
$289 = c^2$
$c = 17$ ft

a = 51 in.
c = 85 in.
Find b.
$a^2 + b^2 = c^2$
$51^2 + b^2 = 85^2$
$b^2 = 7225 - 2601$
$b^2 = 4624$
$b = 68$ in.

Find the missing side of the right triangle.

1. a = 6 ft   b = 8 ft
    10 ft.

2. a = 24 m   b = 7m
    25 m.

3. a = 16 m   b = 30m
    34 m.

4. a = 5 in.   b = 5 in.
    7.07 in.

5. a = 65 cm   c = 97 cm
    72 cm.

6. a = 15 mm   c = 17 mm
    8 mm.

7. b = 17 ft   c = 19 ft
    8.5 ft.

8. a = 5 cm   b = 12 cm
    13 cm.

9. b = 20 in.   c = 101 in.
    99 in.

10. a = 28 in.   c = 197 in.
    195 in.

11. b = 32 cm   c = 40 cm
    24 cm.

12. a = 8.2 m   c = 9.5 m
    4.8 m.

Radicals

Problem Solving and the Pythagorean Theorem

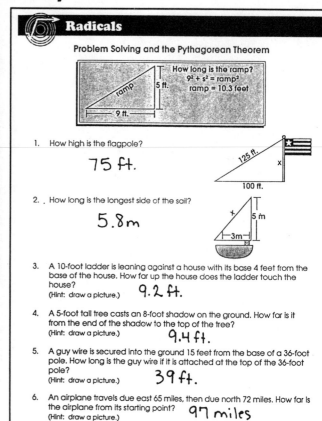

How long is the ramp?
$9^2 + s^2 = ramp^2$
ramp = 10.3 feet

1. How high is the flagpole?
    75 ft.

2. How long is the longest side of the sail?
    5.8 m

3. A 10-foot ladder is leaning against a house with its base 4 feet from the base of the house. How far up the house does the ladder touch the house?
    (Hint: draw a picture.)   **9.2 ft.**

4. A 5-foot tall tree casts an 8-foot shadow on the ground. How far is it from the end of the shadow to the top of the tree?
    (Hint: draw a picture.)   **9.4 ft.**

5. A guy wire is secured into the ground 15 feet from the base of a 36-foot pole. How long is the guy wire if it is attached at the top of the 36-foot pole?
    (Hint: draw a picture.)   **39 ft.**

6. An airplane travels due east 65 miles, then due north 72 miles. How far is the airplane from its starting point?
    (Hint: draw a picture.)   **97 miles**

About the Book . . .

This book has been designed to provide your student with practice in the necessary skill areas involved in mastering Algebra concepts. A review of basic skills is presented in the first part of the book and more specific Algebra topics are introduced on a gradual basis throughout the book. Each skill addressed is identified on all the activity pages and examples of solution methods are included for every skill.

About the Author . . .

Mary Lee Vivian has helped many secondary students master a variety of mathematical skills during her 10 years of teaching in the Parkway School District in St. Louis, Missouri. She holds a Bachelor of Arts Degree in Mathematics from Central Methodist College and a Masters Degree in Business Administration from the University of Missouri – St. Louis. Currently taking time off to be at home with her two children, Mary Lee tutors students in secondary math.

Credits . . .

Author: Mary Lee Vivian
Artist/Production: Emily Georg-Smith
Project Director: Mina McMullin
Editors: Susan Dean, George Van Zwalenberg, Suzanne Hentz
Cover Design: Annette Hollister-Papp